Russell T. Odell
Agronomy Department
University of Illinois

Modern Soybean Production

Modern Soybean Production

Walter O. Scott and Samuel R. Aldrich

FQ The Farm Quarterly, Cincinnati, Ohio 45210

Standard Book Number 911654-79-8

Library of Congress Catalog Card Number 73-113066

The Farm Quarterly, 22 E. Twelfth Street, Cincinnati, Ohio 45210

© 1970 by W. O. Scott, S. R. Aldrich, The Farm Quarterly.

Published 1970

Printed in the United States of America

Contents

1 How the Soybean Plant Grows

2 Variety Selection

3 Seedbed Preparation and Planting

4 Fertilizer for Soybeans

9 Soybeans: Food, Feed and Future

Appendix 175

Index 187

Credits 192

Walter O. Scott

Professor of Crops Extension, University of Illinois

Walter O. Scott, a native Kansan, has been on the staff of the University of Illinois since 1946. He did his undergraduate work at Kansas State College, received his masters from the University of Illinois, and his Ph.D. degree from Purdue University in 1959. It is for his active part in the Association of Official Seed Certifying Agencies that Dr. Scott has received widespread credit for service to agriculture. He is an outspoken advocate of the use of high-quality planting seed in farming. In connection with his knowledge of seed production and certification, Dr. Scott was a consultant in India during a six-week period in 1968 for the Rockefeller Foundation. He has traveled and worked in a number of European countries in connection with his interests in seed certification. In 1967 he was honored in his profession by being named a Fellow of the American Society of Agronomy. He also is a Fellow of the American Association for the Advancement of Science.

Samuel R. Aldrich

Professor of Soil Fertility Extension,
University of Illinois

Samuel R. Aldrich has been on the University of Illinois staff since 1957. Born in Michigan, he completed his undergraduate training at Michigan State University in 1938 and received his Ph.D. degree at Ohio State University in 1942. For 15 years Dr. Aldrich was on the staff at Cornell University, first as extension specialist in agronomy and later as leader in agronomy extension. He is now leader of soil fertility extension in Illinois. He was honored by his contemporaries in 1962 when he was named a Fellow of the American Society of Agronomy, and in 1965, he received the ASA Agronomy Education award. Dr. Aldrich, the author of over 50 articles in leading farm magazines, is perhaps best known in the agricultural writing field as co-author of *Modern Corn Production,* a companion book to this volume. He is also a co-author of *Farm Soils, Their Fertilization and Management,* and he edited *Advances in Corn Production.*

1

How the Soybean Plant Grows

The soybean plant is highly responsive to its environment. The grower can improve this environment by preparing a good seedbed, by limiting weed competition, and by using other practices. He can increase the plant's response to the environmental changes through his selection of variety, planting date, and plant population. The grower can make these decisions more effectively if he understands how the soybean plant grows.

The Soybean Seed

Most mature seeds are made up of three basic parts: the seedcoat, the embryo, and one or more food storage structures. The soybean seed has only two parts. Its two food storage structures — cotyledons — are part of the embryo.

The cotyledons, which account for most of the bulk and weight of the seed, contain nearly all the oil and protein found in the soybean. The cotyledons supply food to the seedling plant for about two weeks during germination and very early growth.

The seedcoat protects the embryo from fungi and bacteria before and after planting. If this protective coat is cracked, the seed has little chance of developing into a healthy seedling.

The soybean embryo has three parts: the radicle, the hypocotyl, and the epicotyl. The radicle, which becomes the primary root, and hypocotyl, which lifts the cotyledons above the soil surface, are located under the seedcoat at one end of the hilum, or seed

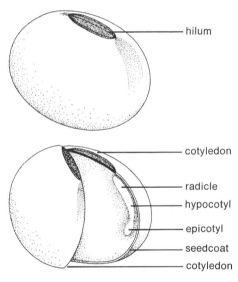

1. A soybean seed is protected from fungi and bacteria by its seedcoat. If the coating is cracked, there is scant chance for a healthy seedling to develop. An opened seed reveals the embryo parts which will become the seedling plant.

scar. They may be seen if the seedcoat is removed, but it is difficult to distinguish one from another without the aid of a microscope. The third part of the embryo, the epicotyl, is the main stem and growing point. It is very small and tucked between the pair of cotyledons.

Germination and Seedling Establishment

The radicle is the first part of the embryo to penetrate the seedcoat. It develops rapidly into a root which must become firmly anchored for the seedling to develop enough leverage to force its way to the

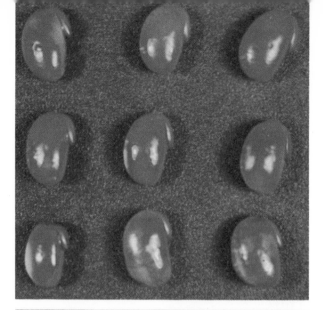

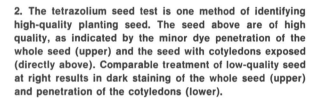

2. The tetrazolium seed test is one method of identifying high-quality planting seed. The seed above are of high quality, as indicated by the minor dye penetration of the whole seed (upper) and the seed with cotyledons exposed (directly above). Comparable treatment of low-quality seed at right results in dark staining of the whole seed (upper) and penetration of the cotyledons (lower).

soil surface. Lateral roots are formed soon after the radicle begins to elongate. And often within four or five days after planting, root hairs appear on the laterals. These hairs are the main absorbing surface of the root system. They are very small and short lived, and might be described as tubular extensions of single epidermal cells. They are formed in the actively growing part of the root just behind the growing point.

The taproot of the soybean plant is less pronounced than taproots of some other legumes, such as alfalfa. Soybean roots branch and re-branch, and within five to six weeks after planting they will reach the center of the conventionally spaced row. By the end of the growing season the roots will penetrate to a depth of five feet or more in a well-drained, good prairie soil. However, the bulk of the roots will be found in the upper 12 inches of soil, with a surprisingly extensive growth in the topmost six inches.

Most of the soybean plant's nitrogen requirements are supplied by nitrogen-fixing bacteria which live in nodules on its roots. The first nodules appear within a week after seedling emergence. Ten to 14 days later, the nodule bacteria are able to supply the plant's full nitrogen requirements. Active nodules have an internal pink color, and new nodules are formed during most of the life of the plant.

After the radicle emerges, the hypocotyl begins to elongate. It forms an arch which is pushed upward through the soil. As the arch breaks the soil surface, it pulls the cotyledons and epicotyl upward. The uppermost cells of the hypocotyl stop growing as cells on its underside continue to grow until the arch is straightened. This process lifts the cotyledons into an upright position.

The epicotyl is exposed to the sunlight when the cotyledons assume a more or less horizontal position.

3. An adequate moisture supply is a major prerequisite to the beginning of the germination process. The radicle, which becomes the primary root of the soybean seedling, is the first part of the embryo to penetrate the seedcoat.

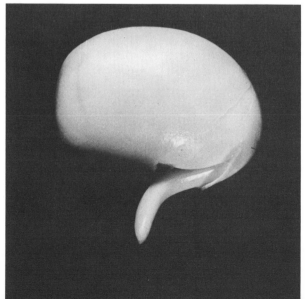

3

4

5

6

At this stage, the plant is prepared for growth as it is commonly recognized.

The first three leaves begin expanding from the epicotyl by the time the cotyledons and epicotyl reach the soil surface. These unfold and develop rapidly following exposure to the sunlight. The first two leaves are unifoliate (only one leaf blade). They are opposite each other and located at the same node. The next leaf and all those that follow are trifoliate (three leaf blades). The trifoliate leaves are located only one at a node and are alternate in position on the stem.

Soon after exposure to sunlight the cotyledons and other plant parts develop chlorophyll and turn green. However, the food stored in the cotyledons remains the main source of nourishment for about a week after emergence. The cotyledons drop after the seedling is capable of supporting itself. Some photosynthesis occurs in the cotyledons, but this contributes very little to the needs of the seedling.

A good supply of soil moisture during the germination period is critically important. The seed must reach a moisture content of 50 percent before the germination processes start. A corn seed, on the other hand, must absorb only 30 percent of its weight in water before germination begins. Because the hypocotyl arch is easily broken when pushed against a solid crust, soil crusting is a serious threat to the germinating soybean.

After emergence, the seedling is tough to kill. This

4. Lateral roots are formed less than a week after the radicle emerges, and then root hairs, the main absorbing surface of the root system, develop.

5. The seedling plant develops root nodules within a week after emergence. Nodule bacteria convert atmospheric nitrogen to forms that can be used by the soybean plant.

6. The seedling emergence stage is one of the most critical for the soybean plant. A crust can cause the hypocotyl arch to be broken under the pressure of the emerging plant.

is surprising when it is considered that the meristem (main growing point) is above the soil surface in contrast to that of corn, which is protected underground until the plant is about knee high. The cold tolerance of soybean tissue is high. Temperatures that kill young corn back to the soil line may damage no more than the uppermost parts of the young soybean plant. While the meristem is at the apex of the shoot, dormant buds capable of producing new stems are present where the cotyledons, the unifoliate leaves, and one or more of the trifoliate leaves join the main stem. As long as the apical meristem is active and healthy, the other buds remain dormant. But if this meristem is killed by frost or hail at least one, and often two, of the dormant buds will become active meristems and produce new stems. If the plant is severed or killed back below the lowest dormant buds, regrowth is impossible.

Vegetative Period

Most crop plants have two major growth stages — the

7   8   9

10   11   12

vegetative stage and the flowering or reproductive stage. In the case of the soybean plant, the period between emergence and the appearance of the first flower — usually six to eight weeks — is the vegetative period. The ultimate size of the plant and the total number of flower positions largely depend on its length and the environmental conditions prevailing during this period.

The soybean plant is photoperiod sensitive, which means that it makes the transition from vegetative to flowering stages in direct response to day length. The key to its flowering mechanism is the length of darkness during a 24-hour period. Most soybean varieties begin flowering soon after the day length begins to shorten. Therefore they are said to be short-day plants. Flowering of southern-grown varieties is initiated by a shorter day than that of varieties adapted to the northern region. At New Orleans, Louisiana, on July 3 there are about 14 hours between sunrise and sunset; at Winnipeg, in Canada, there are about 16 hours. A variety adapted to Louisiana is selected to start flowering when the day length is 14 hours or less. In the Winnipeg area this variety would flower in the middle of August when the day length at that latitude finally shortens to the necessary 14 hours. Conversely, if a variety adapted to the northern area is moved south, it will begin flowering much earlier than if kept in its own area of adaptation.

The size attained by a soybean plant before flowering depends on the environment. The amount of

7. After the hypocotyl has emerged from the soil, it must straighten itself to lift the cotyledons through the soil.

8. Upon exposure to light, the upright cotyledons begin to open. This indicates that the first leaves will soon appear.

9. As the cotyledons continue to separate, the first structures to appear are two unifoliates (single-bladed leaves).

10. The first two leaves grow rapidly in the sunlight, making way for the development of the next leaves.

11. The first trifoliate (three-bladed leaf) appears soon after the unifoliates develop. All other leaves are trifoliates.

12. The soybean plant displays an uncanny determination to survive. When its main growing point, located in the end of the growth shoot, is removed, buds at the leaf axils, heretofore dormant, are activated to produce new stems.

vegetative growth occurring after the initiation of flowering depends not only on environmental factors but also the growth habit. Some varieties are indeterminate in growth habit, some are determinate.

Indeterminate varieties increase their height by two to four times after flowering begins. In the central and northern soybean production regions, where plants begin flowering when 12 to 14 inches tall, this presents no problem. Indeterminate varieties are used in these regions.

Determinate varieties increase their height very little, if at all, after flowering. Customarily, these varieties are grown in the South. Southern soybean plants are considerably taller than 12 to 14 inches

13

Hours and minutes between sunrise and sunset

	New Orleans	Memphis	Champaign	Minneapolis	Winnipeg
May 4	13:24	13:42	14:01	14:24	14:49
9	13:31	13:51	14:12	14:37	15:08
14	13:39	13:59	14:21	14:49	15:22
19	13:45	14:06	14:31	15:00	15:36
24	13:50	14:12	14:38	15:10	15:48
29	13:55	14:19	14:45	15:19	15:59
June 3	13:59	14:23	14:52	15:26	16:08
8	14:02	14:27	14:56	15:31	16:15
13	14:04	14:30	15:00	15:35	16:20
18	14:04	14:30	15:00	15:36	16:22
23	14:04	14:30	15:01	15:37	16:22
28	14:04	14:30	15:00	15:36	16:20
July 3	14:02	14:28	14:56	15:32	16:16
8	13:59	14:24	14:52	15:25	16:09
13	13:58	14:19	14:45	15:19	16:01
18	13:50	14:14	14:40	15:12	15:50
23	13:46	14:07	14:32	15:02	15:38
28	13:40	14:00	14:28	14:51	15:24
August 2	13:34	13:52	14:14	14:39	15:11
7	13:26	13:43	14:03	14:29	14:55
12	13:19	13:34	13:53	14:19	14:39
17	13:11	13:25	13:41	13:59	14:23
22	13:03	13:15	13:29	13:45	14:05
27	12:54	13:04	13:16	13:30	13:47

14

when flowering begins. Use of indeterminate varieties under such conditions would lead to greater plant height and increase danger of lodging. However, some plant breeders are directing serious attention toward the development of short-growing, lodging-resistant, indeterminate varieties for the South. Conversely, breeders are trying to develop determinate varieties for the northern region to reduce plant height. Determinate varieties branch more profusely than indeterminate varieties.

Flowering Period

Flowers are produced where leaf petioles join the main stem or branches of the main stem. The junction of these plant parts is an axil. The flower branch originating at the axil is called a raceme.

The number of flowers that may be produced in a single leaf axil varies greatly among varieties and between locations on the plant. Environmental factors such as temperature and moisture supply during the flowering period also affect the number of flowers on each raceme. The flowering period is relatively long

13. The soybean starts to flower soon after the day length begins to shorten. This table, set up on five day increments, shows that there are more daylight hours on a given date in the northern region than in the southern region (red figures). The flowering of northern varieties necessarily is initiated by a longer day than that of southern varieties. A southern variety that starts flowering when there are less than 14 hours of daylight will flower at New Orleans about July 8. Flowering occurs progressively later (blue figures) the further north the variety is used, until the variety flowers in mid- to late-August at Winnipeg. This, of course, is unacceptable in the north, because the variety will fail to mature before it is killed by cold weather.

14. The photoperiod response of soybeans was demonstrated by accident when these soybeans grew under an illuminated sign at the University of Illinois airport. The plants in the foreground a few feet from the sign received enough hours of darkness each 24-hour period to reach a reproductive stage. Plants near the sign were subjected to continuous light and remained vegetative.

for soybeans. There are reports of as much as six weeks between the appearance of the first and the last flowers. Three to four weeks is considered normal for most varieties.

Flowering characteristics of determinate and indeterminate plants are somewhat different. An indeterminate plant usually blooms first at the fourth or fifth node. Flowering progresses upward. Many new leaves and leaf axils are developed after the first flowers appear on this type of plant. Pods are formed near the base of the plant before the last flower appears at the top.

A determinate plant starts blooming at the eighth

15

16

17

or tenth node. Flowering progresses both downward and upward from this point. Since all, or nearly all, of the axillary buds are in existence when the first flower appears, the progression of flowering from the bottom to the top of the plant is rapid. On this type of plant the racemes terminating the main stem and its branches are quite long. These commonly produce more flowers than racemes located elsewhere on the plant. The plant blooms for a prolonged period because flowering progresses relatively slowly from the base to the tip of each raceme.

The soybean flower is only six to seven millimeters in length. It is self-pollinated (the pollen produced within a flower fertilizes the ovary of the same flower). The soybean plant does not form a pod for each flower it sets. Up to 75 percent of the flowers produced by a plant may fall to the ground. The tendency to abort perfectly healthy flowers is a major concern of the soybean scientist. The key reason for, and prevention of, this loss are unknown. The plant loses more blossoms during periods of hot, dry weather than under more favorable conditions. However, weather and fertility conditions that might be considered ideal do not prevent blossom drop. The Lee variety, a highly popular choice of southern growers, sets enough flowers to produce 250 bushels per acre, yet it is rare to find a crop exceeding a 60-bushel per acre average.

The ability to produce more flowers than pods, and to do this over an extended period of time, makes the soybean less susceptible than some other crops, such

15. Indeterminate varieties, grown in the northern region, set their first flowers and pods in the leaf axils near the base of the plant. As the plant continues to grow in height, new flowers and pods appear progressively higher.

16. Determinate varieties, commonly used in the southern soybean region, attain most of their growth before flowering begins. They develop a relatively long raceme in each leaf axil. Flowering and pod set begin at the base of the raceme.

17. The soybean flower, just six to seven millimeters long, holds the secret keys to solving immense problems in the management and breeding of the crop.

as corn, to short periods of adverse weather during flowering.

Pod and Seed Formation

There is no sharply defined transition from flowering to the pod and seed-formation stage. Pods, withered flowers, and newly opened buds may be found at one time on the same plant, often at the same node. This is particularly true of indeterminate varieties. Both flowering and pod set tend to be more intense and more uniform in the determinate types, but there is still some variation on a single plant.

Few pods are set by the earliest flowers. The first pods appear ten days to two weeks after the first flowers appear. Pod set, once started, proceeds at about the same speed as flowering. Under normal conditions it will be essentially complete in three weeks. The rate of pod growth and seed enlargement is relatively slow at first, but picks up rapidly as flow-

18. A determinate variety bears an unusually long raceme on the end of its main stem. In the middle of the flowering period this raceme may carry flourishing blossoms, withered blossoms, newly formed pods and older pods simultaneously.

ering comes to a halt. Dry matter accumulates in the seed at a relatively rapid and constant rate for the next 30 to 40 days. There is little difference between varieties in the rate of dry matter accumulation. Yield differences are largely a result of the length of time that dry matter accumulates in the seed.

The seed filling period is the most critical time in the life of the soybean plant. Anything that interferes with plant functions during this time can reduce yields, according to research at Iowa State University. For example, if a hailstorm causes a 100 percent leaf loss when the beans are beginning to fill, there can be more than an 80 percent reduction in yield. While the maximum number and size of seed is controlled genetically, the actual number and size produced is largely determined by conditions prevailing during the seed filling period. Moisture stress is especially serious. Dry weather during seed filling will not only reduce seed size, but may also reduce the number of seed per pod. If the stress is serious, small pods may even abort. Adequate moisture during the seed filling period may completely overcome the effects of moisture stress during the flowering period. At Urbana, Illinois, an inch of rain in excess of the normal for an eight-day period during the seed filling stage increased yields by at least 1.5 bushels an acre. This effect is almost twice that of an identical rainfall earlier in the season.

The plant actively accumulates nutrients from the soil during most of the pod and seed formation period.

The plant draws about 30 percent of its potassium and 40 percent of its phosphorus and nitrogen from the soil after the seed filling stage begins. In contrast, corn at the same stage has satisfied all of its potassium needs and 70 percent of its total phosphorus and nitrogen requirements.

Maturity

A newly formed soybean seed contains nearly 90 percent moisture. Early in the bean filling period, and again as the bean matures, the moisture content declines rapidly. The initial reduction takes the moisture content to 65 to 70 percent. From this point moisture content decreases slowly to 60 to 65 percent, while the seed accumulates dry matter and grows in size. As dry matter accumulation is concluded, moisture content declines to 10 to 15 percent in a matter of one to two weeks. This sharp, rapid drop in moisture sometimes causes the crop to become too dry for optimum harvesting, and results in heavy shattering loss shortly before, or at, combining.

The seed continue to accumulate dry matter after the leaves of the plant begin to lose their green pigment and turn yellow. The seed crop finally reaches its maximum dry weight when all the leaves are yellow and half of them have fallen from the plant.

A mature soybean plant has the same high degree of cold tolerance as a young plant. The nearly mature seed normally remains highly viable after exposure to below-freezing temperatures.

19. Vivid changes occur within a soybean pod in the final weeks of maturity. These pods, collected on a single day from varieties of three different maturities, show how the bean changes in shape, size, and color as it matures. The mature bean is at the top, the most immature bean at the bottom.

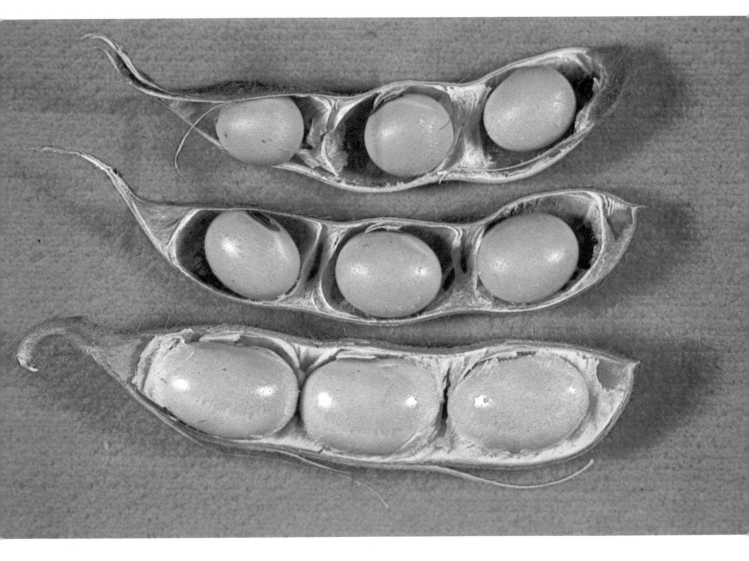

2

Variety Selection

It is important to select a soybean variety adapted to conditions in the field where it will be grown. High yield is much more likely when the strong and weak points of the variety and field coincide. For example, if a disease is prevalent, a resistant variety should be grown; if a weed infestation exists, an early-maturing variety that might be smothered by weeds should be avoided.

Several main characteristics are considered in selecting a soybean variety. They are as follows:

Maturity

Because of their response to photoperiod, most soybean varieties are adapted for full-season growth in a band usually no wider than 100 to 150 miles from north to south. North of this band, the variety will flower later than normal. South of it, the variety will mature earlier.

Effect of location on maturity of Lincoln* soybeans

Location	Latitude	Date Mature
Madison, Wis.	42°34′	October 2
Dwight, Ill.	41°8′	September 27
Urbana, Ill.	40°8′	September 17
Eldorado, Ill.	37°52′	September 8
Sikeston, Mo.	36°32′	August 30
Stoneville, Miss.	33°25′	August 12

*Lincoln was a popular variety in the middle Corn Belt in the 1940's and would be considered as adapted to central Illinois (Urbana).

Soybean varieties usually are placed in 10 maturity classes designated from 00 to VIII. The range in maturity within a group may be as much as 10 to 18 days. Varieties in the 00 group are the earliest in maturity and are adapted to the northernmost production areas of the United States and southern Canada. Group I and II varieties are used in the northern areas of the United States. Group II and III varieties are adapted to the central Corn Belt.

The varieties in group IV and V are used primarily on the east coast and in the upper and central South. Varieties in groups VI and VII are grown in the Southeast and the West, as well as Louisiana, Arkansas, Tennessee, and Mississippi. Group VIII varieties are quite late and are used mostly near the gulf.

In some cases it is important to match maturity to a particular field. For instance, a relatively early variety may be the better choice for a field with fine textured soils that have a tendency to be wet and cool. A later-than-normal variety may have plenty of time to mature and produce high yields on the coarser, well-drained soil that is likely to be drouthy when rainfall is below normal. Early varieties should be avoided in fields where weeds, especially the tall broadleaves, are likely to get out of hand. Harvest problems will be reduced if the soybeans and the weeds can dry up at about the same time.

Generally, varieties that take advantage of all or most of the growing season will yield more than those that mature earlier. There are, however, some ex-

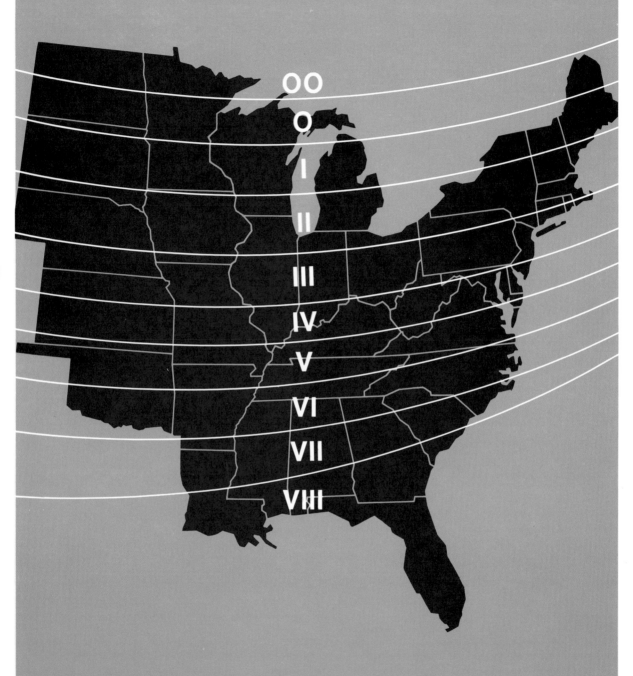

1

OO
O
I
II
III
IV
V
VI
VII
VIII

1. There are 10 maturity classes of soybean varieties. Those varieties adapted for use in southern Canada and the northern-most area of the United States are designated 00, and are the earliest maturing. The higher the number, the later the maturity and the further south the variety is adapted for full-season use. The lines across the map are hypothetical. There are no clearly cut areas where a variety is or is not adapted.

2. The grower should consider the characteristics of each field in selecting soybean varieties to be planted. On well-drained fields (foreground) late varieties can be expected to mature and produce high yields. Early-maturing varieties should be planted on cool, wet-natured soils (background).

2

ceptions to this among the newly released varieties.

There are also seasons when the early variety holds an advantage over the later varieties. It may escape the effects of some quirk in the weather, such as a late drouth. For example, the effects of moisture stress are especially serious when drouth occurs during the time the soybean seed are filling — particularly during the early part of this period. A late drouth may catch the mid- and full-season varieties at the wrong stage of development while the early variety produces normally.

Planting varieties with varying maturities can spread the harvest and sometimes help get more beans in the bin. This may be true even though the early varieties are grown at some yield sacrifice. The staggered maturity reduces the risks associated with weather that makes beans shatter and overdries them to the point that cracking occurs during harvesting and handling.

Earlier varieties are usually favored when fall-seeded small grains follow soybeans. In many areas, full-season varieties can be expected to mature and be harvested under normal weather conditions in time for small grain to be planted. But if maturity is delayed by cool weather or harvest by wet weather, the earlier variety is the better choice.

The use of early varieties for late planting is seldom justified. However, an early variety may be the only one that will have time to mature on rare occasions when hail, a late flood, or some other hazard makes abnormally late replanting necessary. The most important decision in this type of a situation is whether replanting is required. Soybeans, because of their response to photoperiod, are better adapted to late planting in emergencies than most other crops. Even for soybeans, however, good growing conditions immediately following late planting are very important. To be successful, the late planted soybeans must germinate and emerge quickly and grow rapidly after emergence. The photoperiodic response, which insures that plants will mature in less than the normal time, also means a shortened plant and lower pods.

Lodging Resistance

Lodging resistance is highly important in selecting a soybean variety. In Iowa tests, yields were reduced 13 percent when plants were lodged. In Ohio tests, harvest losses ranged from 9.8 to 19.3 percent over a five-year period. Twenty-eight percent of the total loss was credited directly to lodging and to the failure of cut stalks to enter the machine, largely a result of lodging.

Resistance to lodging is one of the characteristics that plant breeders are trying to improve. Their task is complicated by the fact that the highest yielding variety is not always the one with the strongest stalk. Varieties that stand well where lodging is known to be a problem may be the most profitable, even though they have a slight yield disadvantage in variety tests. After all, profits depend on bushels harvested, not

3

Plant population affects lodging

Pounds of seed per acre	Lodging score
25	1.8
50	2.2
75	2.7
100	3.3

3. Lodging, one of the greatest restrictions to high yield, is controlled partly by variety selection. Some varieties offer a valuable, built-in resistance to lodging. Plant spacing also affects lodging. The greater the plant population, the greater the tendency to lodge, as shown in the above.

simply bushels grown.

Planting date and rate influence the severity of lodging. When planting is delayed beyond the optimum date, lodging tends to increase slightly.

Research results indicate that reducing row width from 38 or 40 inches to 20 or 30 inches has little effect on lodging if the population is held at the optimum for the narrower rows. As rows are narrowed still more, some lodging can be expected.

As plant population increases, soybean stems become more slender, internodes longer, and plants taller. As a result, the ability to stand decreases. Planting rate should be matched to the variety and the field. If the variety is somewhat weak in standing ability, the population should be at the low end of the optimum range, but not low enough to encourage excessive branching. Large branches near the base of the plant tend to break off and contribute to harvest losses.

Additional Characteristics

Height of the lowest pods and shattering are important characteristics to consider in selecting a variety. For instance, shattering is more likely to be a problem on drouthy soils. Therefore, on such soil, the grower should plant a shatter-resistant variety.

Disease Resistance

Varieties that offer resistance or tolerance to the soybean cyst nematode and phytophthora rot should

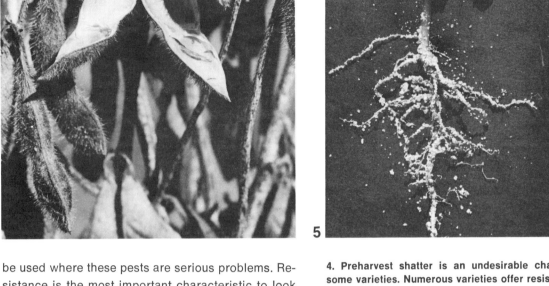

4

5

be used where these pests are serious problems. Resistance is the most important characteristic to look for. This may place quite a restriction on the number of varieties suitable.

Market Quality, Special Markets

Market quality does not rank high on the list of factors to be considered in choosing a variety in the northern half of the soybean production area. Market quality is a result of conditions causing excessive splits and foreign material. These are mainly problems of weed control, proper timing of harvest, and proper combine adjustment.

But in certain areas of the South and along the east coast, market quality is affected by variety. In these areas, several days of wet weather accompanied by high temperature are likely to occur as the soybeans are nearing maturity or are about ready to be harvested. This is the type of weather that encourages the development of pod and stem blight. It may reduce the market quality as well as the yield of the soybeans. Purple stain is another disease in this area that may be linked to market quality. Where these diseases are likely to occur, resistant varieties should be grown. Early-maturing varieties are most likely to be damaged by pod and stem blight because they will mature when temperatures are high.

Most soybeans grown today are processed for oil and protein. On the other hand, a few varieties have been developed for specialty markets. The major ex-

4. Preharvest shatter is an undesirable characteristic of some varieties. Numerous varieties offer resistance to shattering, and should be used when possible.

5. Phytophthora rot, a plant disease especially troublesome in low, poorly drained areas of fields, may appear on higher ground in wet seasons. This plant, susceptible to the disease, has collapsed after inoculation with the fungus organism. Many varieties are resistant to this disease.

ample is the large-seeded, edible soybeans. These varieties produce seed up to twice as large as the normal soybean. Varieties of this type should be planted only for specialty markets.

There are two market outlets for large-seeded soybeans. Both are relatively small, and production for them is usually under contract. One market is for soybeans used in domestically manufactured food products; the other is for export of food-type soybeans. The export is primarily to Japan where the soybeans are used in the manufacture of food products, primarily miso. Kanrich is one variety used in miso. Hawkeye variety is exported to Japan for the manufacture of tofu.

Plant breeders are able to manipulate the protein and oil content of the soybean genetically. Two varieties higher in protein than those commonly grown have been released. These are Provar and Protana. The major market for these is likely to be for export to countries processing soybeans for human food.

Selecting a Variety

Before choosing the variety best adapted to his con-

6

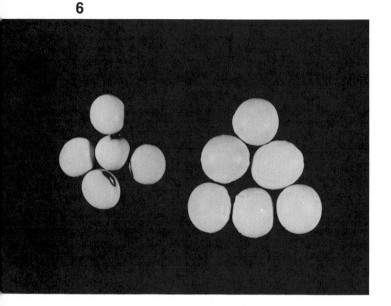

7

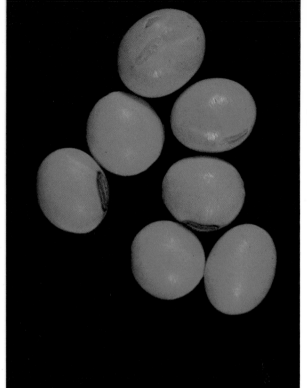

ditions, the grower should consider information concerning yield, lodging, relative maturity, plant height, disease resistance, and other characteristics. This may be obtained from several sources. The county extension agent or vo-ag instructor has the latest information from the state college of agriculture. Many colleges conduct variety performance trials. With their knowledge of the local soil types and weather conditions, the county agent or vo-ag instructor may be able to predict how a new variety will perform.

State and USDA research and extension personnel also can advise growers on varieties. Most currently grown soybean varieties are the result of a cooperative USDA and state experiment station breeding and uniform testing program. A uniform test is one in which research workers located across the country test a basic set of experimental and commercially grown varieties. Since the same varieties and experimental strains are tested throughout the area of adaptation, the state extension or research worker is likely to have a wealth of information on newly released varieties. Varieties developed in privately financed breeding programs are also tested by many state universities and the results are available to growers.

Most reputable seed dealers must keep up to date on what is new in varieties as well as weed and insect control. They are a good source of information concerning the results of college-conducted variety tests. They also know the local performance of varieties

that have been released and are grown by certified seed growers. The local dealer usually is one of the best sources of information on varieties developed by private industry. His role in this area may increase, for it appears that the number and relative importance of private varieties will in all probability increase.

After seeking advice and making his selections, a grower should check new varieties against ones currently used on his farm. Differences in maturity, plant height, lodging resistance, and height of podding may be easily observed. Some fairly accurate observations can be made on a field-to-field basis, but yield differences should be measured only when the varieties are grown side by side on exactly the same soil type and with not greater than a 5-to-10 percent difference in population. The same fertility levels should prevail, too.

In making such a comparison, the grower should plant the number of rows that fits his combine cutter bar width. It may be convenient to have two combine widths across the field for each variety tested. This makes it possible to make a complete round trip on a single variety. The soybeans harvested from each strip should be weighed and checked for moisture content. If a moisture tester is not available, the soybeans can be placed in a tightly sealed glass jar or plastic bag and taken to the local elevator for testing.

The following information is required to calculate yield per acre:

— Exact size of harvested area

6. Some varieties of soybeans grown for specialty markets have larger-than-usual seed. The Kanrich variety, used domestically and exported for the preparation of soy foods, has seed considerably larger than the average.

7. A seed blend, representing two or more soybean varieties, often may be recognized by the difference in hilum colors.

8. The difference between having too many and not enough plants per acre is seen in various ways. One, which occurs during harvesting, is excessive branching. If the planting rate is low, large branches formed at the base of the plant will break off during combining, adding to losses.

— Weight of the harvested soybeans
— Moisture percentage

To determine what fraction of an acre is harvested, calculate the square feet and divide by the number of square feet in an acre (43,560). Multiply the plot yield by the number of harvested areas required to make an acre. Now, using the moisture content of the harvested soybeans, select the number of pounds required to equal a bushel of soybeans containing 13 percent moisture (page 30).

Blends and Brands

"Blend" and "brand" are words that may be new and somewhat unfamiliar to the purchaser of soybean seed.

A "blend" is a particular mixture of varieties or species.

A "brand" is a registered trademark or trade name selected by a company to distinguish and identify the seed it sells.

Blends of soybean seed usually are sold without any identification of the varieties or their proportions in the mixture. The blend is sold simply as "soybeans — variety not stated". The seed of a single variety can be marketed in the same way.

In the case of a blend or brand, the trade name becomes almost synonymous with variety identification. Legally, a brand name may not be used as a variety name, nor used as a part of the variety name, unless the original name of the variety involved the

brand name or trademark. The Federal Seed Act and most, if not all, state seed laws prohibit the use of any variety name other than that given the variety by the originator or the person who first marketed it. These laws also prohibit the mislabeling of seed as to variety. The seedsman has two legal alternatives: one is to sell seed under the original variety name; the other is to make no claim as to the variety of the seed sold. Some seed companies have chosen to follow the second alternative and identify the seed they sell by a trade name or brand. The brand name is frequently used in sales promotion, as a variety name would be used.

The company selling soybean seed without stating the variety is not held legally responsible for the varietal purity of the seed. No claim of variety is involved. The advice to buy seed only from a reputable dealer is good at any time, but especially important when seed is bought by brand identification.

One of the intriguing possibilities of blends is that of spreading risk. For instance, in some areas of the central Corn Belt the severity of the disease phytophthora rot depends on the weather. If it is cool and wet

Moisture equivalents

9

Actual moisture content	Pounds equal to one bushel at 13 percent
8.0	56.74
8.5	57.05
9.0	57.36
9.5	57.68
10.0	58.00
10.5	58.33
11.0	58.65
11.5	58.98
12.0	59.32
12.5	59.66
13.0	60.00
13.5	60.35
14.0	60.70
14.5	61.05
15.0	61.41
15.5	61.77
16.0	62.14
16.5	62.51
17.0	62.89
17.5	63.27
18.0	63.66
18.5	64.05
19.0	64.44
19.5	64.84
20.0	65.25
20.5	65.66
21.0	66.07
21.5	66.50
22.0	66.92
22.5	67.35
23.0	67.79
23.5	68.23
24.0	68.68
24.5	69.14
25.0	69.60

9. To make a quick calculation of yield, the grower must know the total weight of his soybean crop, or a representative sample, and the moisture content. He simply divides the weight by the appropriate figure in the right hand column to get the equivalent of bushels at 13 percent moisture.

Results of an Illinois drill box survey

	Homegrown seed (percent)	Certified seed (percent)
Pure seed content	95.70	98.70
Inert matter content	2.26	1.16
Weed seed content	.02	.00
Other crop seed content	2.06	.17
Germination	80.00	84.00
Pure live seed content	76.56	82.91

after planting, the disease will be a problem, particularly in poorly drained areas of the field. Under good growing conditions, there may be little or no evidence of the disease. Harosoy 63 is resistant to phytophthora rot but the higher yielding Amsoy is quite susceptible. What happens if a field is planted to a blend of the two? In the cool, wet year, the blend should yield more than if Amsoy alone were planted; and in the good growing season, it should do better than if Harosoy 63 alone had been planted. But, a blend seldom outyields its highest yielding component. The yield is more likely to be a little better than the average yield of the component varieties.

Blends vary in performance. At Purdue University, 13 different blends, some involving three varieties and some only two varieties, were tested for four years. The blend with the best average yield was as good as the highest yielding variety. None were lower in yield than the lowest yielding variety, but several were little, if any, better than the mean yield of their components. Results at Iowa State University were similar.

Seed Quality

High-quality seed is just as important in making money with soybeans as it is with other crops. Many drill box surveys have shown that 25 to 50 percent of the soybean seed being planted is low in one or more quality factors. The most important quality factors include:

1. Varietal purity
2. Germination and vigor
3. Mechanical purity and inert matter
4. Weed seed
5. Other crop seed
6. Uniformity of size

Poor appearance may be a pretty good indication of low germination and vigor, but the converse is not necessarily true. A sample of soybeans that won second place at a midwestern state fair was tested for germination after it had been placed by the judges. It germinated 0 percent. The first place sample germinated 99 percent. The third and fourth place samples were also low in viability but 90 percent of the seeds in the fifth place sample grew. All the seed looked equally viable.

Some important information about the quality of the seed purchased from a seedsman appears on the label. A grower who saves his own soybeans for seed or gets them from a neighbor's bin needs the same information about the seed as he would get from a seedsman.

Homegrown soybean seed is likely to be low in one or more quality factors. It should be tested and properly prepared for planting.

Varietal Purity

One of the most important quality factors is varietal purity. The time and special care spent in selecting the best variety for a particular set of conditions may

11. Poor-quality planting seed showing the effect of disease and mechanical damage (above) will not produce results equal to that of high-quality seed (above, left). A visual appraisal does not tell the entire story. Seed should be tested for germination before planting.

be lost unless attention is given to this factor.

The use of certified seed assures high varietal purity. The grower of certified seed starts with seed that is known to have a high degree of varietal purity and he protects his production from contamination. In addition, a representative from an official seed certifying agency carefully checks the varietal purity of the crop in the field, and examines the harvested seed. Certified seed is identified by an official seed certification label.

The grower who keeps his own soybeans for seed should be careful about getting varieties mixed. This can occur easily. Drill box surveys have shown that soybeans can become mixed in only a year's time. This is somewhat surprising when it is realized that soybeans are self-pollinated. Contamination does not occur through outcrossing; it is a result of mechanical mixing. Planting equipment, combines, wagons, trucks, grain handling equipment, and bins contribute to contamination unless carefully cleaned between varieties. In addition, volunteer plants may occur in fields where soybeans follow soybeans, adding to the problem. When the varietal purity changes, the performance changes—usually falling below that of the best variety in the mixture.

12. Excessive and careless handling of planting seed can result in cracked seedcoats. The seed pictured here are likely to be dead, or at least low in germinating power.

12

13

14

13. The presence of weed seed and splits reveals that soybean seed has not been processed properly for planting.

14. The presence of a few corn kernels in soybean planting seed spells a warning of trouble to come. Corn is a serious soybeanfield weed in some parts of the Midwest.

Germination and Vigor

Viability is a quality factor which can be tested. The results of a germination test appear on the label of seed purchased from a seedsman. The field emergence seldom will be exactly the same as the percent germination, but the grower cannot afford to plant seed without knowing the results of a germination test. It is obvious that seed that germinates 90 percent will establish more seedlings per pound than that germinating a mere 70 percent. Less widely known is the fact that seedling vigor — the ability of the young plant to grow rapidly and withstand stress — usually is greatest in the seed with the highest level of germination.

Good quality soybean seed will germinate 80 percent or better. Germination of 90 percent or above is not out of the question. In some areas, seed of this quality is easily obtained. In other areas, high germinating lots of seed are more difficult to find. The soybean is not exactly delicate, but the problem of maintaining viability during the ripening and harvest period is greater than with some other crops.

Mechanical Purity, Inert Matter

The amount of pure seed is something the grower can see. Pure seed is defined by the Association of Official Seed Analysts as the seed that is whole, or if broken, more than one half the original size. The need for a high percentage of pure seed and a low inert content is obvious. Inert matter is just what the

How mechanical condition of seed affects soybean stand and vigor

Seed condition	Percent of seed emerged	Percent vigorous seedlings in stand
No cracked seed coats	80	72
7 percent cracked seed coats	76	69
100 percent slightly cracked	57	41
100 percent severely cracked	43	23

name implies. It includes such things as dirt, sticks, bits of broken soybean seed, and stones.

The pure live seed content of a lot of seed may be obtained by multiplying the percent of pure seed by the percent germination (90 percent germination x 98 percent pure seed = 88.2 percent pure live seed). This in turn may be used as one method of comparing the value of different lots of seed. A bushel of soybeans with a germination of 90 percent and a 98 percent pure seed content holds 52.92 pounds pure live seed (88.2 percent x 60 pounds). Assuming that the price of this seed is 10 cents per pound or $6.00 per bushel, the actual cost of each pound of pure live seed is 11.3 cents. A pound of pure live seed in another lot having a germination of 85 percent and a purity of 98 percent, selling for $6.00 per bushel, would cost 12 cents. Pure live seed, however, is not the only yardstick of comparison for different lots of seed. The presence of certain weed seed or other crop seed may be considered more objectionable than a difference in the pure live seed content.

Weed Seed, Other Crop Seed

The presence of weed seed can be detected by careful inspection. Several weed seed are so nearly the size of soybeans that removal is difficult, but sophisticated cleaning machines can do it. Most of the weed seed found in drill box surveys occur in homegrown seed or that grown by neighbors.

In some areas, seed of other crops is a serious contaminate. Corn is probably the most widespread of these; however, sunflowers are also considered serious in some areas. Both of these crops are weeds in the soybean field. They compete for water and plant food, and the presence of their seed may lower the grade of commercial soybeans.

Uniformity of Size

A uniform stand is obtained most easily with seed of uniform size. While uniformity of stand is perhaps not so important in producing a good yield of soybeans as that of some other crops, it is logical to assume that the highest yield is more reachable with a uniformly spaced, optimum number of plants per acre.

Another advantage of uniformity in seed size is evenness in emergence. Soybean seed of equal size are more likely to be similar in seedling vigor. Perhaps the most important advantage of uniform seed size is that it is evidence that the seed has been processed, a good indication that some of the undesirable weed seed, splits, and inert matter have been eliminated.

Variety Improvement

Plant breeders are looking at new and different leaf shapes and new plant shapes. They are constantly seeking new sources of resistance to disease, insects and lodging. The plant physiologist is looking deeper and deeper into the metabolic processes within the plant. He is interested in the enzyme systems within

15. It is probable that the practical production of hybrid soybean seed will require natural transfer of pollen from one plant to another. This simple scheme for producing hybrid seed is based on the use of the honey bee to carry pollen from plant A to flowers on plant B, a male sterile seed parent. It is assumed that plant A carries the restorer. Maintenance of the male sterile B is not shown. Seed produced on plant B will be harvested and sold for planting.

The hybridization of soybeans

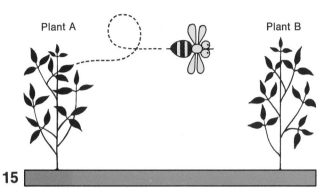

Plant A   Plant B

15

the plant. From this type of basic research may come answers to questions like, "Why does the soybean abort 25 to 75 percent of the flowers it forms?"

Hybrid Soybeans

The secret of producing hybrid soybean seed on a commercial scale is yet to be discovered. The problem is that the soybean flower is a perfect flower. Both the staminate and pistillate parts are present in the same flower. When pollen is shed, it immediately drops on the stigma (the pollen-receiving part of the pistil) in the same flower. This often happens before the flower opens (blooms).

Therefore, the first step in producing a hybrid is to prevent self-pollination in the seed parent. This is a particularly tough step. It can be done by hand, but the job is tedious because the flower is very small. The stamens must be removed with a pair of tweezers before they shed pollen. Pollen is then collected from the desired paternal parent and transferred to the flower. A person may be able to make as many as 200 cross-pollinations per hour — as long as he can stand the strain. The artificially cross-pollinated flower or the pod it produces may abort the same as a naturally self-pollinated flower. Therefore, the plant breeder counts on an average of about one seed per cross made.

Some chemical or genetic means of preventing self-pollination in the seed parent must be discovered before hybrid soybean seed can be produced on a commercial scale. The genetic route appears to be the most promising and is now receiving the greatest attention.

Preventing self-pollination is only the first step. There will still be the problem of moving pollen from the pollen parent to the seed parent. There may also be the problem of genetically restoring fertility in the planting seed.

Researchers are exploring means of transferring soybean pollen by insects. Of particular interest is the honey bee. This insect is often found working soybean flowers. Perhaps a strain may be developed that will prefer soybean flowers.

The plant breeder makes crosses hoping to find offspring possessing all of the good characteristics and a minimum of the poor characteristics of both parents. When such an offspring is found, it becomes a homogenous, stable line or variety.

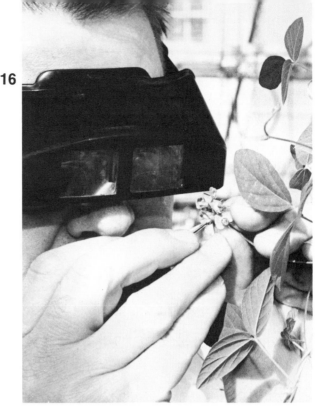

16

16. Cross pollinating soybeans by hand requires skill and patience. The plant being used in this cross has unusually small leaves, and is one of thousands of strains plant breeders scan in the search for useful traits.

17. The exacting nature of artificial cross-pollination of soybeans may restrict a man's output to 200 crosses an hour. One half or more of the pollinated flowers may abort.

17

3

Seedbed Preparation and Planting

The art of seedbed preparation now is about where fertilization was 10 to 20 years ago. Many farmers, unsure of where they can safely cut corners, continue to use the time-worn tillage practices of the past. Conventional seedbed preparation methods for a given locality and soil type may be safer than reduced tillage systems, but every grower should consider the changes he might make to save time and soil without sacrificing yield. In some cases, it may even be profitable to take a slight yield reduction if tillage costs can be reduced enough to increase net return per acre.

Good seedbed preparation provides:

—A place for seeds to germinate quickly

—An environment in which seedling roots can obtain moisture and nutrients

—A good kill of annual weed seedlings and a severe setback to perennials

—Management of crop residues to permit efficient use of planting and cultivating equipment

—Good surface tilth that will prevent a crust and capture and hold needed rainfall.

Requirements for Germination

Soybeans require a more moist soil than corn for germination. Putting it another way, a soybean cannot take on moisture from a nearly dry soil as well as corn. Besides, soybeans must absorb 50 percent of their weight in water to germinate, compared to only 30 percent for corn.

1. The best soil-to-seed contact usually occurs in a well pulverized seedbed. If the fine particles are gently firmed around the seed, moisture is transferred to the seed quickly, providing for quick germination.

2. The silhouettes of three types of planter seed furrows at the moment of seed drop are revealing. A standard sword opener (top) is less than ideal for planting soybeans because the seed is lost in a two-inch furrow. Soil-to-seed contact may be poor unless very fine soil fills the seed furrow. A double disk opener (center) creates a V-shaped furrow and the seed rolls down until it rests firmly against the sides. A pinnacle may be formed under the seed location, however, allowing the surrounding soil to dry prematurely. A sliding opener that slices a V-shaped furrow (bottom), the Acra-Plant, is considered by some to provide the best soil-to-seed contact.

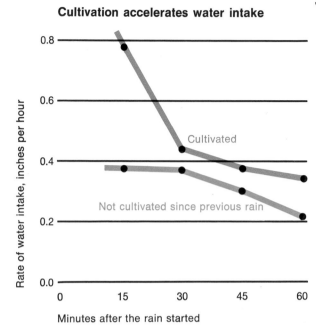

Cultivation accelerates water intake

In a soil containing plenty of moisture, soybeans will germinate, even if the seedbed is coarse. But when the soil moisture is ideal for planting, seeds germinate quicker if surrounded by fine material. This is because the seed must take on moisture from contact with soil particles or from the humidity of the air within the soil. If the seedbed is coarse, cloddy, and open, the humidity will be low during dry periods. The soil moisture will occur in the small pores and in thin films on the soil particles. If coarse soil aggregates touch the soybean seed at only a few places, transfer of moisture to the seed will be ineffective. But if the seedbed is relatively fine and gently firmed around the seed, moisture can transfer at maximum speed, thus favoring quick germination.

Requirements for Root Growth

The factors affecting germination also apply to efficient moisture and nutrient uptake by roots. But the seedbed between the rows need not be firmed as much as that within the row because soybean roots soon turn downward, and thus are likely to be in moist soil. Also, rainfall usually firms the soil shortly after planting.

Having the plow layer quite loose between rows helps plants to stand a rainy period because the roots can get oxygen from large pockets of trapped air. On the other hand, a fine seedbed is better if the weather is dry during the early part of the growing season while the soybean roots are still shallow.

3. Cultivating to break a crust is an effective way to increase water intake on a fine-textured soil. The cultivated area absorbed water almost twice as fast as the uncultivated area during the first 30 minutes of rainfall.

4

4. The moldboard plow, basic implement for primary tillage in many regions, efficiently turns sod and crop residues.

Tillage for Weed Control

Quackgrass, Canada thistle, sow thistle, Johnson-grass, and other perennial weeds can be controlled best by fitting the seedbed well in advance of planting and repeating the treatment, if necessary. Soybeans can then get a head start on the weeds and be up and ready for cultivation before the weeds recover.

If annual weeds are the main problem, one thorough kill at or just before planting is often just as effective as harrowing three or four times at weekly intervals. If the annuals start unusually early and appear to be getting out of hand, one harrowing two or three weeks before planting time is justified, but may be difficult to work in the schedule if other crops are being planted at the same time.

The wide range of pre-emergence herbicides provides several options in early control of weeds when treatments are combined with tillage at or slightly before planting time. Annual weeds can often be reduced by using planting methods that leave the seedbed between the rows loose so weed seed cannot germinate. This works in dry years, but not when rains keep the surface wet.

A planter that drags a shoe through the soil cannot be used effectively where there is loose, coarse crop residue on or in the soil surface. On the other hand, units with rolling furrow openers can plant efficiently in such a field. Some planters have disks that clean the row area but leave the residues between the rows.

Residue Management

Where herbicides give complete weed control there is little concern for trash between the rows. But when chemicals and cultivators are used in combination, the amount and coarseness of crop residues must be adjusted to the equipment. Few problems are more aggravating than a cultivator that continually clogs with trash, tears out rows, and forces the operator to back up and clean the sweeps.

Maintaining or Improving Tilth

Sands and sandy loams can be worked at any moisture content. Silt loams and clay soils, if worked when wet, become cloddy and hard upon drying. On the other hand, if they are plowed and harrowed at just the right moisture content, the number of granules or aggregates can be increased temporarily. Many such aggregates will not survive for long under a beating rain, but they are helpful while they last.

Primary Tillage Operations

Primary tillage breaks sod, buries trash and residues, kills weeds, and loosens the plow layer. The main tools are the moldboard, chisel, and disk plows, as well as the lister. The rotary tiller also functions as a primary tillage implement.

Moldboard Plow

The moldboard plow, unequaled for breaking tough

sod and turning under green manure crops, covers heavy straw, cornstalks, and other trash better than any other tool. It also buries weed seed deeply and sets back perennial weeds more than other tools. The moldboard cuts, lifts, shears, and turns the soil to a depth of 5 to about 12 inches. This action improves the plow layer tilth in silty and clay soils when done at the proper moisture content.

A long moldboard works well on a heavy grass sod to turn the furrow slice upside down. A short moldboard creates the greatest shearing force, but tends to stand the furrow slice on edge and leave some residues exposed.

The best depth to plow is a much-discussed subject. Although research shows that eight inches is usually deep enough, deeper plowing has sometimes produced slightly higher yields. In special cases, plowing very deep to mix layers of sand and clay has been profitable. A rule of thumb is to use a plowing depth about one-half the width of cut, in order to get good turning of the furrow slice. Plowing not only changes the rate at which rainfall enters the soil, but also changes the soil's capacity to hold water before run off begins.

Fall plowing with a moldboard has little advantage, if any, as far as soybean yields are concerned. But it will normally allow earlier planting than spring plowing. The advantages of fall plowing are as follows:
— The slowest part of seedbed preparation is accomplished before the busy season.

— If the spring is wet, planting is more likely to be done on schedule if secondary tillage is all that remains to be done. This is of less importance for soybeans than some other crops, such as corn.
— If clay soils are fall-plowed when too wet, winter freezing and thawing will mellow the clods and improve the structure, thus correcting the mistake.
— Fall-plowed soils having more than 30 percent clay will firm down to about the right degree, whereas spring plowing of these soils sometimes must be followed by several harrowings.

Fall plowing also has some disadvantages:
— The soil is more exposed to wind and water erosion. These risks are minimized by leaving the furrow as rough as possible, not turning under all of the residue, avoiding fields that have light residues such as soybeans or other types of beans, and leaving narrow, unplowed strips at right angles to the prevailing wind direction.
— Soils that are high in silt but low in clay tend to run together or slake down into nearly their preplowed density. Sometimes replowing in the spring is necessary, but usually one disking or field cultivation will be adequate.
— A frozen plowed surface is very rough for spreading manure or fertilizer.

If the soil has more than a three percent slope, fall plowing should be done on the contour. From central Ohio through Indiana, Illinois, and Iowa, fall plowing

5

5. The chisel plow has become increasingly popular for fall tillage, often being used in the same field where combines are operating. The chisel plow may be used in the spring, also, but is relatively ineffective in wet soil.

on the contour is safe on soils with up to six or seven percent slope. South of that line, where the soil is frozen for a shorter period or not at all and winter precipitation is higher, the safe slope is three to five percent.

Chisel Plow

The chisel plow loosens and shatters the plow layer, provided the soil is not too wet. In wet soil the chisel merely cuts a slit. Chiseling is faster than moldboard plowing. It also requires less draft and reduces wind and water erosion by leaving plant residues on the surface.

It is common practice to chisel one direction in the fall and chisel crosswise in the spring. Some residue is worked into the soil, some is left on the surface to reduce erosion and promote the entry of rainfall. Residues insulate the surface, thus keeping it cooler and wetter. This is an advantage during hot, dry weather, but may be undesirable in the spring when such a condition delays planting and slows seedling growth. This is far more important for corn, which benefits greatly from early planting, than for soybeans.

Chiseling, best adapted to fields where residues are fine and not too heavy, works very well on soybean stubble. This is fortunate because wind and water erosion are much worse following soybeans than corn. Corn stubble, which has a heavier root system, plows up much rougher than soybean stubble.

Chiseling in the Midwest is, therefore, a substitute for moldboard plowing when corn follows soybeans.

When chiseling replaces moldboard plowing, broadcast phosphorus and potassium are concentrated in the surface few inches. The chisel plow has some disadvantages: It is ineffective when the soil is wet; it does not turn under sod, or bury weed seed, or plant residues.

Disk Plow

The disk plow works well on bare ground or small grain stubble, especially in regions with less than 25 inches of annual rainfall. Once over with a disk plow nearly completes seedbed preparation. Most of the trash and residues are worked into the soil. In dry regions this helps to control wind erosion and also increases water penetration. As little as 250 pounds of residue per acre on the soil surface greatly reduces wind erosion during the winter and early spring. Disk plows do not turn over heavy sod enough to kill the grass.

Lister

A lister throws soil both ways from the row area, leaving a furrow in the middle. This type implement is used in semi-dry regions and in the southern states. Under dryland farming conditions, it has the following advantages: (1) The plants can stand more drouth, because the root systems are set deeper; (2) The furrows store water for the crop while reducing erosion.

6

In regions with more rainfall, there are three disadvantages of a lister system which places the row in the bottom of a shallow furrow: (1) It is often too wet in the early part of the season; (2) If a crust forms over the row, it cannot be reached easily with a rotary hoe or weeder; (3) If a pre-emergence herbicide fails, an early cultivation carries the risk of covering the soybeans.

In many southern states where listers are used, soybeans are planted on a bed rather than in the trench, avoiding these problems.

Rotary Tiller

The rotary tiller, composed of rotating spring steel hooks or knives, is designed to prepare a seedbed in one operation. Raising the hood tends to leave trash on the surface; lowering it buries residues. The rotors of this implement break up many of the soil aggregates. This makes loams, silt loams, and clays more likely to crust following heavy rains than when other primary tillage tools are used. However, this problem is being reduced by improving the design of the rotating knives and adjusting the rotor speed for various soil conditions. If the pto speed is reduced and the tractor speed increased, a rotary tiller will leave the soil surface in a fairly roughened condition. Rotary tillage is best suited to soils that have a minimum of tilth problems and those that are not likely to crust. The rotary tiller has found popular use in strip tillage, in which the between-row area is left undisturbed.

Deep Chiseling, Subsoiling, and Panbreaking

Farmers often ask if deep chiseling will improve poorly drained soils, or soils with natural hardpans. A few farmer testimonials have been quite encouraging. But carefully conducted research results from several states are not so optimistic. (An exception to this occurred in South Carolina where profile disruption of a Coastal Plain soil with a traffic pan increased soybean yields by as much as 20 bushels per acre in dry years. When rainfall was normal, however, maximum increases were five bushels per acre. At other locations yields were reduced by subsoiling when rainfall was normal).

A farmer should examine his soil closely before deciding if deep chiseling will be beneficial. If the plow sole or pan has been caused by tillage operations, it will begin at plow depth and extend down 4 to 6 inches, making the overall depth 10 to 16 inches. In this case, chiseling may be profitable where the soil does not normally freeze that deep. But in areas where the soil freezes to a depth of 12 to 26 inches, chiseling to break a plowpan is not likely to pay. Ice lenses forming in moist soil naturally lift and loosen the pan unless the soil is very dry. Proof of this action is seen by most farmers in northern states who note how light and mellow the soil is when it first dries out after the winter freeze.

Some soils have a natural hardpan 12 to 18 inches deep, formed by natural processes over thousands of years. Because of a high silt and clay content, it

6. Rotary tillage is particularly useful when time is of key importance, as in the case of soybeans following small grain. Here, the straw has been burned and a rotary tiller is preparing a seedbed in one pass over the field.

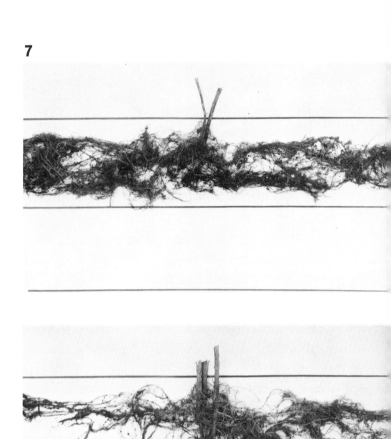

7. The root development of soybean plants grown under three systems demonstrates the influence of tillage. The top plant was taken from a plot disked to a depth of about 6 inches with no other land preparation. Its roots do not even reach the line 6 inches below the indicated soil level. The middle plant, grown where the soil was moldboard-plowed to a depth of about 10 inches, extended its roots somewhat below the 6-inch level. The plant at the bottom was grown after the soil was subsoiled to a depth of 16 to 18 inches. The soil was a Norfolk sandy loam, at Blackville, South Carolina.

stays wet much of the growing season. Since the hardpan is rarely dry enough to fracture, chiseling only cuts a narrow slit and has no lasting effect.

If the hardpan is fractured to permit rainfall to get through, where will it go? Generally, the layers below the pan are also compact and poorly drained. In such a case, chiseling is ineffective because it is impossible to break through to a better drained layer. This is why research shows that subsoiling heavy soils in humid regions rarely increases crop yields, even in the first year.

One way to improve the effect of deep chiseling is to get crop roots to grow into the chiseled zone, helping to keep it open. But this is not easy because the hardpan layer is often strongly acid and low in phosphorus. Placing limestone and fertilizer in the subsoil sometimes temporarily increases rooting within the chiseled zone. But subsoiling, even when combined with deep placement of lime and fertilizer, has not been profitable in any area where the subsoil stays moist most of the time. In South Carolina, however, soybeans produced an extra five bushels per acre for six years where one ton of limestone and 800 pounds of superphosphate were mixed through the top 24 inches of soil. This supports the theory that man-made plowpans or traffic pans may be broken up profitably in soils that do not freeze naturally.

Secondary Tillage

Secondary tillage, which follows primary tillage, is

8. The disk harrow, a basic, secondary tillage implement for most agricultural areas, works well on freshly plowed ground. With the availability of wide models and the suitability of the disk for incorporating certain herbicides, this implement has retained a major role of importance.

designed to accomplish one or more of these purposes: firm and pack a coarse, rough seedbed; loosen a hard seedbed; crush clods; chop trash or sod; kill weeds; smooth the seedbed surface; or conserve moisture.

Moisture is conserved when secondary tillage operations follow right behind the plow, reducing both the evaporative surface and the depth from which moisture can be lost directly into the air. On the other hand, any tillage of a dry surface brings up moist soil, accelerating evaporation. Stirring the surface three to four inches is, in fact, often an effective way to speed up drying and warming of the soil to facilitate planting.

Disk

The disk harrow cuts and loosens the top three to seven inches of soil and buries trash and crop residues. But it packs the soil below cutting depth. A heavy disk penetrates hard ground better than other tools. It works well on freshly plowed sod or fields with loose trash.

Spring-Tooth Harrow

The spring-tooth harrow, replaced on some farms by the disk and field cultivator, digs, lifts, and loosens the top three to five inches of soil. It breaks clods if they are not too hard and refines the seedbed. It effectively pulls out rootstocks of some perennials like quackgrass. It leaves depressions in the surface,

which catch and hold water. It buries little trash.

The spring-tooth does not penetrate hard ground as well as the disk, but is better suited than the disk for stoney fields. When used on freshly plowed sod, the spring-tooth tends to pull sod pieces to the surface. This can be avoided by using a shallow setting of the teeth the first time over and harrowing in the same direction as plowing. The teeth can be set deeper the second time over.

The spring-tooth harrow clogs badly in coarse trash. It does not kill tough perennial weeds as effectively as a disk or cultivator with broad sweeps. The weeds often slide around the narrow teeth.

Field Cultivator

The field cultivator, which does not compact the soil like the disk, has wide sweeps that cut perennial weeds better than the spring-tooth and it leaves the soil surface quite rough, thus reducing wind erosion. The field cultivator digs, lifts, and loosens the soil to a depth of four to seven inches. The sweeps, on heavy stiff shanks, penetrate hard ground well. This implement does not clog in trash as readily as the spring-tooth harrow because the shanks are much farther apart. It is fair for stoney fields though not quite so well adapted as the spring-tooth. The field cultivator is suited to freshly plowed stubble, but not sod, because it brings the sod to the surface.

The field cultivator is an excellent tool for summer fallowing. It leaves the surface open and rough to

9. The field cultivator, followed by a spike-tooth harrow, is an effective one-pass secondary tillage combination for use directly ahead of the soybean planter.

hold water and reduce both wind and water erosion, and its wide sweeps cut weed roots. It is a suitable primary tillage tool (replaces the moldboard plow) on bare fields or following soybeans, field beans, sugar beets, potatoes, and other crops having light residues.

Spike-Tooth Harrow

The spike-tooth harrow is used mainly to smooth and refine the seedbed and break soft clods. It is especially suited to killing small weed seedlings when planting is delayed after the seedbed has been prepared. It is a low-draft tool, most often attached for smoothing behind other tools that leave the soil surface ridged.

Cultipacker

The cultipacker pulverizes clods and firms the surface two to four inches of soil but has little effect below that depth. It is especially useful for compacting and leveling freshly plowed fields. It leaves the surface in low ridges, reducing crusting following heavy rains. It presses small stones into the soil surface. The cultipacker is unequaled for breaking clods. It works well in combination with a spring-tooth harrow because the action of the two are complementary.

Reduced Tillage Systems

Most of the early minimum tillage research was with corn, rather than soybeans. The basic principles are,

however, equally adapted to soybeans because the large seed are planted at about the same depth as corn seed. The reduced danger of crust development under reduced tillage is important for soybeans.

Pioneer farmers never overworked seedbeds because they did much of the work by hand. Later, when working with horses, they seldom overfitted the soil. It was only after tractor power was widely used that overfitting became common.

The amount of compaction from tractor tires hit its peak in the 1950's. Plenty of power was available to work the seedbed and farmers were unaware that overworking was unnecessary, costly, and even harmful in some cases. Now tractors are more powerful and heavier, but wider implements and tandem units are being used, thus making fewer trips over the field.

10. Among the assets of the cultipacker are its usefulness for crushing small clods and the fact that it leaves the soil in low ridges, offsetting the formation of a soil crust.

10

Chemical weed control often replaces one or more cultivations. More residues are returned to the soil from high-yielding crops, too. Probably the greatest danger today is that of eager farmers working wet fields. Extra-wide tires, while distributing the weight of a tractor over more surface area, carry at least one threat. They bring compaction closer and closer to the row, particularly in cases where a farmer switches to narrow rows.

Reducing tillage operations cuts expenses, promotes water entry (thus reducing runoff and erosion and storing more water for dry periods), controls blowing of the surface soil, reduces compaction, and allows row crop production on land that is otherwise too steep for safe cropping. Yield increases sometimes result but cannot be considered a primary goal.

The term "conservation tillage" has crept into farmers' jargon. It refers to all practices that help reduce wind or water erosion. Reduced tillage is often an important part of conservation tillage.

Methods for Reducing Tillage

■ Once-over on plowed ground or light stubble. Three possible systems are:

1. Mount cultivator sweeps or rotary devices on a tool bar ahead of the planter to smooth the surface and kill weeds in the row or entire area.

2. Spray herbicide — either band or broadcast — as tractor pulls planter over the field. Note: A broadcast application may cost more than cultivation combined with planting.

3. Harrow once, then plant either as a separate or combined operation.

These systems eliminate several trips over fall-plowed fields and fields that work up unusually well in the spring. They may replace conventional plowing or listing on light stubble such as that of soybeans, cotton, potatoes, and other crops which leave fields more erosive than corn does. These systems produce yields equal to those from conventional methods and require no special equipment (though special equipment is available).

■ Planting directly on plowed ground. There are two versions:

1. Wheel-track planting. This should be done closely behind plowing. Otherwise, the furrow slice may become too dry or, in heavy clay soils, clods may become too hard for a good seedbed in the wheel track. Also, weeds will start in wet periods, necessitating a tillage operation unless a completely dependable herbicide can be applied at planting time. This works on all light-textured soils and the clay soils where soil tilth is good and soil moisture is just right. Planting can be done when the soil is slightly too wet to disk or harrow. There is a disadvantage: plowing must be delayed until near planting time, resulting in a peak load of work at planting time.

2. Plow-plant. This system, in which a planter is attached to or mounted on the plow, is suited to about the same conditions as wheel-track planting.

11. The soil on the right half of this field is loose and porous, a result of the use of minimum tillage. It has absorbed the rainwater, in contrast to the conventionally tilled soil on the left, which is slow to absorb water.

The furrow slice must be well turned and mellow. A device is needed to compress the furrow slice and fill voids ahead of the planter shoe. The row must be on, rather than between, furrow slices unless the soil is very crumbly. Because of these requirements, the system is best suited to sandy and silt loam soils. Plow-plant will work successfully on clay soil if the farmer learns to judge when the moisture content is just right and knows how to prepare the row area.

Like wheel-track planting, plow-plant calls for delayed plowing. This is a disadvantage for farmers with large acreages, especially on heavy (fine-textured) soils in wet springs.

■ Strip tillage. This method, involving preparation of the row area only, has been tried but has not caught on widely. The International Harvester Company first introduced its Till Planter in the early 1950's. More recently, machines have been developed to till the row area with sweeps, rotary hoes and rotary tillers. The main problem following corn is how to cultivate without having the stalks clog up and bury the soybean seedlings. Also, pre-emergence herbicides are less effective with heavy residues on the surface. This can necessitate early cultivation just at the time when it is impractical because of the residues.

In sod, the problem is to find an herbicide that is fully dependable under all weather conditions. Strip tillage will prepare a suitable seedbed in the row on fall-plowed or freshly plowed fields.

■ Zero tillage, no-till planting. This method involves planting in a narrow slit opened by a shoe or coulter in otherwise undisturbed soil. Sometimes the field is covered by sod; other times it is in small grain stubble; and on some occasions, the field was in a row crop the preceding year. An herbicide is broadcast to control grass and weeds because the crop cannot be cultivated unless, of course, the land was in a row crop the preceding year.

The most important advantage of zero tillage is that it permits row crops to be grown on slopes too steep for conventional seedbeds. Other advantages are a savings in time and fuel, successful use of smaller tractors, elimination of a plow and secondary tillage tools, and an opportunity to plant in soil too wet to till or plant in a conventional system. Also, soil crusting is not a problem.

Zero tillage in small grain stubble is used in double cropping with soybeans. At least five points should be checked before double cropping with zero tillage:

1. Is suitable planting equipment available? Several manufacturers offer implements for use under these conditions.

2. Can planting be finished in time for the crop to mature? North of a line through central Missouri and Illinois, southern Indiana, and Maryland on the Atlantic coast, it is difficult to plant soybeans on time

12

13

12. One method of strip tillage involves the use of a power-driven rotary tiller with planter units attached.

13. Zero tillage in sod killed by herbicides was used first in corn production, but is now used for soybeans also.

after the harvest of winter wheat, barley, or oats. The line is considerably farther south at high elevations in the Appalachians.

3. What are the chances of having adequate soil moisture for germination and production of a profitable yield? State experiment station specialists and weather records can provide information useful in making these estimates. In double cropping, zero tillage increases the available moisture two ways. First, it avoids the losses associated with tillage. Second, an excellent mulch is provided, reducing soil temperature and evaporation of moisture from the surface.

4. Can weeds be controlled by chemicals alone? The answer is likely yes.

5. What should be done with the grain stubble? Some farmers burn off the straw and stubble to the dismay of soil experts; others simply bale the straw and plant in the stubble. Under some conditions, soils have held up under double cropping and straw burning for several years. It is doubtful, however, that this practice can be used without long-term harm to the soil. Some of the greatest proponents of minimum tillage leave the straw on the field, and plant and cultivate through it without problems. The use of a straw chopper on the combine assures that the small grain residue will not be troublesome.

Zero tillage in sod is used primarily for corn, but is gaining in popularity among soybean growers in some areas. The concerns are similar to those dis-

cussed for planting in stubble, with these differences: Planting can be finished earlier than in stubble, even if one cutting of hay is removed beforehand; the farmer has to contend not only with weeds, but with the sod crop itself; a sod crop continues to use moisture until it is killed while the small grain stops using moisture about two weeks before harvest; field mice and other rodents are more often a problem.

Continuous zero tillage for row crops allows the use of quite steep slopes. This may be a great advantage to farmers that have only hill land. However, if the amount of residue is large, such as following high-yielding corn, special problems may occur. The soil dries more slowly, thus delaying planting. This is very important for corn, but less so for soybeans. (Slow drying is an advantage in mid-season when moisture conservation is desired.) Also, the soil stays cold longer, a particular disadvantage for corn in northern states, but of less importance for soybeans. In addition, cultivation requires special care, so a thorough weed kill by herbicides is essential. And finally, surface residue often interferes with the action of the herbicide. Weeds under the residue may escape the weed killer.

Soil Conservation

The public at large is becoming concerned over the preservation of environmental quality. More and more attention is being given to the effect of farming practices.

Every duststorm, flood, sediment-filled reservoir, and muddy river brings closer the point at which laws may require changes in farming practices. Such changes could increase costs and reduce efficiency. In the long term, the public will likely have to share part of the cost. Commercial farmers are, to a considerable extent, responsible for water runoff and wind and water erosion. They are custodians of the soil. They farm most of the best land. They cannot, in good conscience, say that the problem belongs to someone else.

The job of keeping the land intact takes on a new dimension when viewed not over the life of the current farm operator but over thousands of years. Fortunately, profitable farming is compatible with preserving, or even improving, soils for the future. Laying out contours, planning terraces, and designing dams and outlets are jobs for experts. County extension agents may help with general decisions. Soil Conservation Service technicians are available for planning more complex engineering.

Suggestions for good farming practices that contribute significantly to soil and water conservation are:

Fit the cropping system to each soil on the farm. It may be best to grow row crops continuously on the least sloping fields and devote steeper land to small grains and long-term sod.

Follow an adapted reduced-tillage system. Minimum tillage leaves the surface in better condition for

14. No-tillage planters make it possible to plant soybeans right behind the combine in double-cropping systems.

15. Soybeans planted in small grain stubble have the benefit of an effective mulch. Soil moisture is the most critical factor in this type of planting.

water to enter, thus reducing runoff and erosion.

Use fertilizer to promote conservation. High-yielding crops help protect the soil surface during the growing season and add organic matter which improves tilth, increases water intake, and reduces erosion.

If feasible, leave residues on the surface. This preserves structure and keeps the surface from sealing over under the beating action of rain.

Fall-plow gentle slopes carefully. Plow across the slope and leave the surface rough. A rough surface catches and stores the most water. Avoid secondary tillage of fall-plowed ground.

Planting

Should the time of planting soybeans be based on the calendar date or the soil temperature? The answer depends on the location and whether the variety is full-season or early for the locality.

In the lower one-half to one-third of the southern soybean production region, the soil temperature is great enough to germinate soybeans before the day length is long enough to prevent early flowering. In this area, the calendar date, because it is an indicator

16

16. Ordinary water erosion, once the exclusive concern of farmers and a limited number of scientists, has become an important point of public concern.

17. Wind erosion becomes a major issue when it restricts public utilities. This type of erosion has increased in some areas where large acreages are devoted to soybeans, which leave little crop residue in comparison to corn.

of day length, is the best measure of when to plant. North of this area, soil temperature or some other factor may be the better yardstick.

Day Length and Planting Date

Response to day length determines whether a variety is early or late in maturity. The minimum number of hours of darkness required to induce flowering is the factor that separates the early from the late-maturing varieties. The very early varieties, adapted to the northern production area where the days are long, will flower under almost continuous daylight. The very late varieties, adapted to the shorter day area of the South, require at least 10 hours of darkness before flowering is initiated.

Any variety — early or late — will begin to flower within 30 days of emergence when the daylight period is only 12 hours long. Forty-five to 60 days between emergence and flowering is normal. When this vegetative period is shortened, the effect on the soybean plant is usually a reduction in both yield and height.

In the southern region, where varieties in maturity groups VI, VII, and VIII are normally grown, 14½ hours of daylight is the first criterion in deciding when to plant. Dr. E. E. Hartwig of USDA has demonstrated this in studies at Stoneville, Mississippi. Adapted varieties planted in May at Stoneville start blooming about 60 days after emergence. These same varieties planted in early or mid-April bloom within 40 to 50 days. The early planted soybeans produce less, and

grow shorter in height, than those planted in May.

Allowing for the twilight periods between daybreak and sunup and between sunset and nightfall, the day length on April 10 at Stoneville is about 13¾ hours. By May 1, it lengthens to 14½ hours. The early planted soybeans, which emerge when the daylight period is less than 14½ hours in length, flower too early to make maximum vegetative growth. The flowering period and the beginning of the pod and seed formation period occur under longer-than-normal day-length conditions. These growth stages progress at a slower-than-normal pace.

There is very little difference in the time of maturity of April- and May-planted soybeans. Day length affects all phases of the soybean plant's life. Longer-than-normal days slow up development; shorter-than-normal ones hasten it.

Temperature and Planting Date

The threshold temperature for germination is around 50 degrees. Unless the temperature is increasing steadily, planting when the soil is in the low 50's may not be advisable. Emergence occurs very slowly when the soil is cold. Additionally, the seedling is subject to attack by soil organisms and it is a poor weed competitor under cold soil conditions. A seedling will emerge five to seven days after planting when the soil temperature reaches the middle and upper 60's.

The soil is often hot and dry when soybeans are

17

planted following a small grain crop in a double-cropping system. Ideally, soybeans should not be planted when the soil temperature is high unless sufficient moisture for rapid germination is present or assured. Soybean seed loses vigor when subjected to high temperature. This is particularly true if the humidity is also high. The combination of high temperature and high humidity may be encountered under field conditions, as well as in a storage bin. There may be just enough moisture in the soil to start germination, but not enough to finish it. The vigor and vitality of the seed will decrease rapidly under high temperature conditions, and stands may be poor.

Other Factors that Influence Date of Planting

Throughout most of the northern soybean production region, corn competes with soybeans for time and equipment. Where both crops are grown on the same farm, it may be more profitable to plant corn before soybeans. Corn suffers a proportionally larger yield decline as a result of planting delays than do soybeans. The three-year yield of Clark, a full-season variety, at Urbana, Illinois, declined an average of 3.6 percent as planting date was delayed from early May to the last of May or the first of June. Conservatively, it can be estimated that the same delay in planting corn would cause a loss of 10 to 20 percent in yield.

The study of Clark variety also included Shelby, Harosoy, and Chippewa. Shelby matures 7 to 10 days earlier than Clark; Harosoy, about three weeks earlier; and Chippewa, a month earlier than Clark. Shelby, like Clark, produced best when planted in early May. The yields of both Harosoy and Chippewa were highest when planted in late May. The yields of all four varieties declined rapidly when planting was delayed past early June. The results of this and similar experiments lead to these conclusions:

■ Varieties that require most of the growing season to mature will produce their highest yield when planted as soon as the soil temperature or day length will allow. The yield of these varieties usually declines as planting is delayed. However, the loss in yield is relatively minor for the first two or three weeks of delay; after that, the loss is likely to be much more severe.

■ Early varieties often do not respond to early planting. They usually produce higher yields when planting is delayed for two to three weeks. Selecting the best planting date may be more critical in the case of early varieties. Their yields tend to peak during a relatively short period. For instance, the yield of Harosoy at Urbana when planted in late May was 2.5 bushels per acre higher than when planted earlier, and about 7 bushels per acre more than late June plantings.

Calendarizing Harvest Dates

The exact day that a field will be ready to harvest depends to some degree on temperature and mois-

18

18. This plant, growing under short-day conditions, has not reached normal height and will produce a low yield. This illustrates the need to use a tall-growing, adapted variety for late planting. It also shows the importance of having enough moisture for immediate emergence and rapid growth of late-planted soybeans.

19. Planting before May 1 and a 14½ hour daylight period in the South reduces both the height and yield of soybeans.

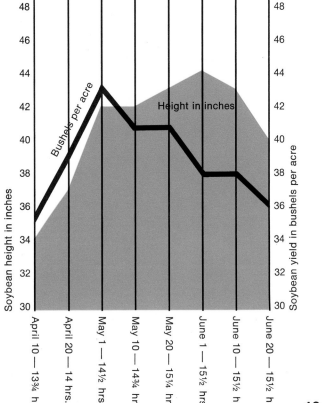

Soybean height in inches

Bushels per acre

Height in inches

Soybean yield in bushels per acre

50 — 50
48 — 48
46 — 46
44 — 44
42 — 42
40 — 40
38 — 38
36 — 36
34 — 34
32 — 32
30 — 30

April 10 — 13¾ hrs.
April 20 — 14 hrs.
May 1 — 14½ hrs.
May 10 — 14¾ hrs.
May 20 — 15¼ hrs.
June 1 — 15½ hrs.
June 10 — 15½ hrs.
June 20 — 15½ hrs.

19

Data: E. E. Hartwig, USDA

ture supply during the growing season. The grower can, however, manipulate varieties and planting dates in such a way that one field will be ready to harvest before another. To stagger the harvest, he should select varieties that differ by two to three weeks in maturity.

The calendar date on which a full-season variety reaches maturity is not influenced much by planting date. For instance, Roanoke, planted June 10 at Stoneville, Mississippi, matured only four days later than when it was planted 40 days earlier on May 1. Similarly, the date on which a full-season variety ripened at Urbana, Illinois differed only 11 days for a 42-day difference in planting date. This shows that the opportunity to manipulate harvest date by changing date of planting of full-season varieties is limited.

The earlier a variety is, the more its date of maturity is influenced by planting date. At Stoneville, Mississippi, Odgen, an early variety, matured 18 days before full-season Roanoke when they were both planted on the first of May. Only nine days separated them when both were planted on June 10.

If a grower is using varieties that differ by only a week in maturity under normal conditions, the earlier

variety should be planted before or immediately after the later variety. When the spread in maturity is greater, the need for planting the early variety before or near the time of the later variety is not so great.

The Effect of Planting Date

In the Corn Belt, mid-May planting produces taller plants than planting at earlier or later dates. The height of the early varieties decreases proportionally more than that of later varieties as planting is delayed past mid-May.

In the South, later varieties obtain their greatest height when planted in late May or very early June. The early varieties tend to decrease in height as planting is delayed past early May.

The effect of planting date on the height of soybeans is one reason why mid- or full-season varieties should be used for late planting as long as there is a reasonable chance for them to mature before a killing frost. Late planting has these additional effects:

— Lodging tends to increase. However, the choice

20

The effect of short days on soybeans

Planting date	Emergence to first bloom (days)	First bloom to maturity (days)
April 10	47	142
May 1	63	109
June 1	55	95
June 10	44	87

21

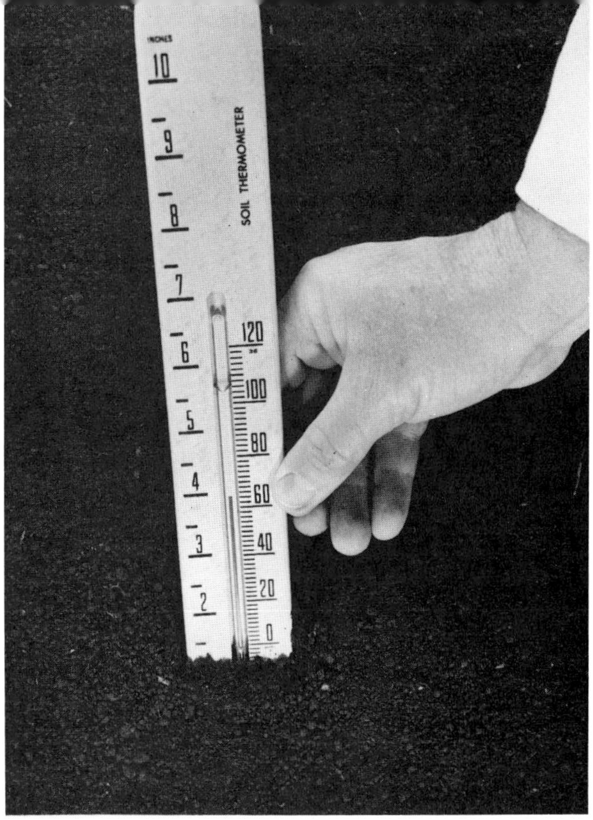

20. Short days hasten blooming in the early part of the season, and maturity in the latter part.

21. When the soil temperature at seed placement depth is in the mid- to upper 60's, soybeans can be expected to emerge five to seven days after planting.

of variety has a much greater influence on lodging susceptibility than planting date.

— Seed quality usually improves. This is true because seed formation and ripening occur when temperatures are cooler. However, late planting may be harmful to seed quality if the crop is caught by a severe frost.

— The oil content tends to decrease slightly. This will usually be accompanied by an increase in protein content.

— Seed size may or may not be affected. It is influenced by the favorableness of the environment during the pod-filling period. A change in planting date may or may not make this coincide with unfavorable moisture and temperature conditions.

— Seed shattering, a varietal characteristic, normally decreases with later maturity.

Planting Rate

Planting too much seed is probably more common than planting too little. The soybean has a tremendous ability to compensate for variations in population. Therefore, the penalty for over or underplanting is relatively small.

This may also explain why the planting rate recommended by research and extension workers varies little from north to south and from east to west. From 8 or 10 to 12 good seed per foot of row in the traditional 36- to 40-inch row is almost a universal recommendation. In the South, where weeds grow large and control is often difficult, there is a tendency to favor the upper rate. Texas A&M recommends the rate be increased so there will be 10 to 12 surviving plants per foot of row.

As row width is narrowed, planting rate should be adjusted. Results of studies in the regions where narrow rows are used indicate that optimum populations are: 6 to 8 plants per foot of row at harvest time in 30-inch rows, 4 to 6 in 20-inch rows, 3 to 4 in rows 10 inches or narrower. Use of the smaller or larger plant population should depend on the fertility level of the field, lodging resistance of the variety, and the conformation of the variety to be used. Varieties having susceptibility to lodging or a strong tendency to branch may do better at lower populations; those that are more resistant to lodging or do not tend to branch will do better at higher populations. Also, recent research indicates that the penalty for over or underplanting the nonbranching varieties may be more severe than those that tend to branch profusely at low populations.

Lodging is the character most often affected by increasing population. Yet moderate lodging may be less harmful to yield than underplanting.

22. In most cases, the yield penalty for delayed corn planting is severe. On the other hand, the penalty for a delay in planting soybeans does not become severe until after June 1. This is why corn is planted before soybeans.

Soybeans are tolerant to delayed planting

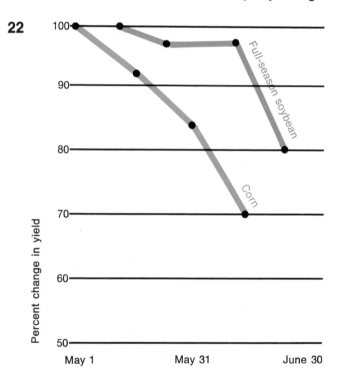

Increasing the population within the row tends to increase the plant height and lodging. It also increases the height of the lowest pod. However, varietal selection affects pod height more than small differences in population density. The number of branches, pods, and seed per plant usually decreases as population increases. Other characteristics such as oil content, protein content, and seed size of most varieties are relatively unaffected by normal variations in populations.

Many rate-of-planting recommendations are given in bushels or pounds of seed per acre. This is a very general recommendation because of the great difference in seed size among varieties and between environments. Sixty pounds of Lee may contain 30,000 to 40,000 more seed than 60 pounds of Hood produced under the same conditions. Environment also influences size. In the Uniform Soybean Tests conducted by the United States Regional Soybean Laboratory, the size of Harosoy 63 seed varied by 20 percent between two locations in Illinois in 1967. In that same year, seed of Lee grown at Halfway, Texas was 32 percent larger than that produced at Portageville, Missouri.

A difference of less than 25 percent in seed size can usually be overlooked, because over or underplanting by as much as 25 percent usually has little influence on yield. But a difference of 30 percent in seed size plus 10 percent in germination can easily threaten the success of a crop. The knowledge that

23. Planting rates should be reduced as rows are narrowed. A general recommendation is to have 10 plants per foot of row in 40-inch rows (top); 8 plants per foot in 30-inch rows (middle); and 6 plants per foot in 20-inch rows (bottom). The drawing makes it easy to see that if the planting rate for 40-inch rows is used in 20-inch rows, 30 plants will be crowded into the area normally allotted to 20 plants.

soybeans are able to compensate for population variation is comforting, but not necessarily protective. The first step to maximum yield is planting high-quality seed at the rate that best fits the field, the row width, and variety.

When the intention is to have eight plants per foot of row at harvest, only the viable seed planted should be counted. The required number of seed should be increased by about 10 percent for each time the field is rotary hoed.

For example, assume that a grower wants to have a stand of 10 Lee soybean plants per foot of row. Planting is to be in 40-inch rows. Weed conditions in the field make it likely that one rotary hoeing will be required, so the population is raised by the suggested 10 percent to 11 plants per foot of row. Since there are 13,068 linear feet of row per acre in 40-inch spacings, the desired number of plants per acre is 143,748 (11 x 13,068). It takes 3,350 average Lee seed to make a pound (page 57), so 43 pounds of viable seed are required per acre (143,748 ÷ 3,350). The particular lot of seed in question contains 85 percent pure live seed (page 33), meaning that the planting rate should be increased by 15 percent. The pounds of seed to be planted per acre is 49.5 (115% x 43).

Planting Depth

Planting depth has an important influence on the number of seedling plants that emerge. One and a half to two inches is about the maximum depth from which soybeans can emerge in most soils. The ability to emerge successfully from deep planting differs among varieties and is influenced by soil type, but all soybeans emerge slowly when planted deep.

The danger of insect and disease damage increases materially with slow emergence. The same is true of herbicide damage.

Breaking the arch of the hypocotyl during emergence, usually caused by a soil crust, can result when seed are planted deep and subsequent heavy rain packs the soil.

How two varieties differ in emergence

Variety	Percent emergence at three planting depths		
	2 inches	3 inches	4 inches
Amsoy	91	68	6
Clark	79	8	0

Source: Iowa State University

Row Width

In the northern and central regions, soybeans planted in narrow rows consistently yield more than those grown in traditional 40-inch rows. In the South, where varieties of the determinate growth type are grown, a response to narrow rows is the exception rather than the rule.

Where narrow rows are recommended, soybeans in 20- to 30-inch rows have a 10 to 15 percent greater

average yield than those in 40-inch rows. Generally, in such areas, the recommendation is to use rows as narrow as the necessary weed control methods will allow. This means that the width of tires on the cultivating tractor usually limits the degree to which rows can be narrowed. In Illinois tests with Wayne soybeans, yields continued to increase as rows were narrowed from 40- to 10-inch spacings.

Shorter and earlier varieties benefit more from the use of narrow rows than taller, later varieties. And the benefit from using narrow rows increases as planting is delayed past the optimum date. Late-planted southern soybeans may respond to narrow rows because they are reduced in height.

**Average yield of three soybean
varieties at two planting dates**

Planting date	Variety	Row width (bushels per acre)		Increase (percent)
		40-inch	20-inch	
Late May	Acme	18.2	22.4	23
	Merit	30.5	36.1	18
	Chippewa	35.6	39.5	10
	Average	28.1	32.6	16
Mid-June	Acme	19.4	27.2	40
	Merit	27.1	34.5	27
	Chippewa	31.1	35.0	12
	Average	25.8	32.2	28

Adapted from research at the University of Minnesota

24. The grower should adjust his planting rate to the variety in question. A variety that branches profusely when spaced at the rate of 8 plants per foot of row (right) will produce more beans at this spacing than if crowded at a rate of 12 or 14 plants (center and left) per foot of row.

The potential yield advantage for producing soybeans in narrow rows has been recognized in the central Corn Belt for as long as the crop has been economically important. Acceptance of narrow rows, however, has been cool, due to the problem of controlling weeds (and the need to have room for cultivators to operate), plus the inconvenience and cost of maintaining two sets of equipment in a corn economy geared to 40-inch rows. Neither of these problems has been solved completely, but improvements in herbicides have greatly reduced the weed hazard for both corn and soybeans. New corn varieties that do well at high populations in narrow rows are making it practical to own one set of narrow row equipment for both crops.

According to University of Illinois agricultural economists, the corn-soybean farmer who has a large acreage of soybeans may be able to finance the switch from 40- to 30-inch row equipment with the increased returns from the soybeans alone. In this example, the farmer changes from four-row, 40-inch to six-row, 30-inch planting and cultivating equipment. He also changes from a two-row combine head for the 40-inch rows to a three-row head to accommodate the narrow rows. Considered in the example are

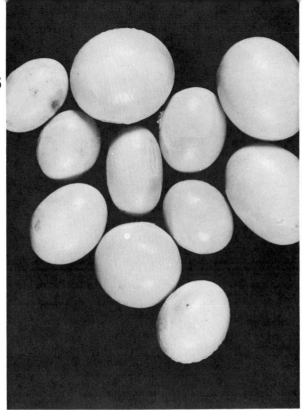

25. The variation in seed size may be great, even within a single field. This may cause planting rates to vary.

additional costs of the narrow row equipment and increased cost of seed and herbicides. The example also allows for a modest saving in labor. The economists conclude that a farmer growing 200 acres of soybeans needs only a two-bushel-per-acre increase to pay the additional costs. Any increase in excess of two bushels of soybeans, or any improvement in the yield of corn, represents profit.

In the central and northern regions, the benefits of producing soybeans in narrow rows are sure to increase as varieties and herbicides improve.

Planting Systems

Because of its versatility, the soybean is grown in many different cropping systems. There are several unusual planting practices—some beneficial, some not so beneficial:

■ Alternating strips of corn and soybeans.

The outside row of corn normally yields more than those inside the field. This observation logically leads to the question of whether alternating strips of corn and soybeans might yield more income than when the two crops are grown separately. Alternate rows, alternate pairs of rows, and alternate blocks of four to six rows have been tested in the Corn Belt. Corn benefited from the lack of shading, and yields were higher. Soybeans suffered from the additional competition for sunlight, and yields were reduced. The overall result in a majority of cases was no advantage over planting each crop separately.

The variation in seed per pound

Maturity group	Variety	Approximate number of seed per pound
00	Altona	2750
	Portage	2700
0	Grant	2800
	Merit	3250
I	A-100	2400
	Chippewa	2900
II	Corsoy	2750
	Harosoy 63	2550
III	Adelphia	2900
	Wayne	2750
IV	Custer	2950
	Clark 63	3000
V	Hill	3350
	Dare	3100
	Dyer	2850
VI	Lee	3350
	Davis	3000
VII	Bragg	2900
	Semmes	2850
VIII	Hampton	2750
	Hardee	3100

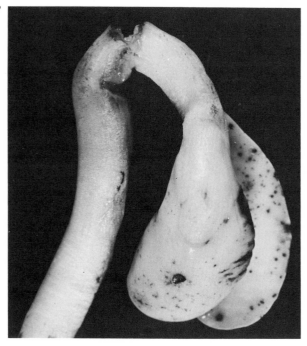

27. A broken hypocotyl arch may be caused by deep planting, a crust, a compacted soil, or a combination of these.

28. In the Midsouth, soybeans sometimes are planted in the "out" rows of skip-row cotton, particularly when the cotton pattern is four rows in and four out. Cotton, the more valuable of the two crops, is well established before the soybeans are planted, usually on only two rows. This minimizes the chance of soybeans competing with the cotton.

■ Alternating strips of cotton and soybeans.

Among southern farmers there has been some interest in planting soybeans in skip-row cotton. The disadvantages of such a system probably outweigh the advantages. The most serious problem is the danger of contaminating the soybeans with cotton insecticides and defoliants. The laws concerning chemical residues in soybeans are quite strict. Also, the practice is most feasible in four-and-four cotton, and there are some years in which the cotton program puts this system at a disadvantage.

■ Interplanting soybeans with soybeans.

Interplanting an early variety between the rows of a later variety after first cultivation allows the production of soybeans in narrow rows with conventional 40-inch planting and weed control equipment. Results of Illinois tests show no yield advantage for this practice. The fact that total yield was not reduced might suggest the possibility of using the idea where there has been a problem in establishing a stand and the grower wonders whether the surviving stand is adequate.

■ Alternating soybeans of differing plant type or maturity.

Alternate rows and alternate pairs of rows of Jackson and Lee varieties, which differ in height by 12 to 15 inches and about 12 days in maturity, were tested in Mississippi. The yield from the alternating strips

was equal to the mean yield of the two varieties, showing that the idea has no value over conventional pure-stand planting.

■ Interplanting soybeans with forage crops.

Seeding ryegrass or Crimson clover between the rows of eight-inch tall soybeans at Wooster, Ohio did not reduce the yield of the soybeans. Seeding either vetch, red clover, alfalfa, or a mixture of vetch and ryegrass depressed yield.

■ Double rows.

Experiments involving sets of two rows close together separated by the traditional 40-inch row have shown no advantage in yield and some disadvantages with respect to weed control.

■ Row direction.

Tests in the Corn Belt and Canada show no advantage for planting soybeans in north-south rows over east-west rows.

■ Corn, soybeans in same row.

The planting of corn and soybeans in the same row for grain has been tested. Both crops are harvested for grain in separate operations. An early maturing corn variety is used. It is combined while the soybeans are still green; the soybeans are harvested later. However, research in Georgia indicates that greatest returns can be expected when the two

crops are grown separately. The yield of both crops was greater when they were grown alone than when grown in combination.

■ Hill dropping versus drilling.

Occasionally someone who plants corn in hills forgets to change the planter to drill for soybeans. The consequences are significant, although not as great as usually expected. Drs. J. W. Pendleton and F. W. Slife, University of Illinois, compared the two methods in 1952.

Hill dropping versus drilling

Space between hills in 40-inch rows	Plants per hill	Yield in percent of drill-row yield*
20	5	85
20	10	88
20	15	93
10	5	91
10	10	92
26⅔	10	91

*Drill-row soybeans were planted at the rate of 10 seeds per foot of row.

■ Planting in standing small grain.

Double cropping, the practice of growing a crop of soybeans following another crop such as small grains, is relatively common in some areas. The success of late-planted soybeans depends on having enough moisture to favor rapid germination and growth. Minimum soil preparation and no-tillage sys-

tems often pay off in double cropping.

Since moisture is not always in good supply after small grain harvest, the possibility of planting the soybeans in the standing small grain prior to harvest has been explored. The results of experiments show that the success of this practice is just as dependent, if not more so, on a favorable moisture supply than that of waiting until after harvest.

■ Aerial seeding small grain in soybeans.

The University of Kentucky suggests the aerial seeding of small grain, particularly winter wheat, in standing soybeans. The early establishment of small grain in this fashion has these advantages:
— Erosion is reduced.
— Cost is usually no greater than that of drilling.
— Labor that is saved may be used in more timely harvest of soybeans and corn.
— Periods of excessive soil moisture need not stop the seeding operation.

The disadvantages of aerial seeding include the fact that higher seeding rates are necessary and dry or unfavorable conditions can delay germination and reduce stands.

■ Broadcast and Aerial Seeding

Soybeans planted in rows usually outyield those that are broadcast seeded. Often, the higher yield in rows is the result of better weed control through cultivation. However, planting in rows has other advan-

29. The seed on the far right are treated with inoculant, and will produce healthier plants than the untreated seed if planted where soybeans have not grown previously.

tages, including more uniform stand and emergence, and a lower seeding rate.

Broadcast seeding with endgate seeder, bulk fertilizer spreader, or airplane is used for the first few years when soybeans are grown on newly cleared land. After the chunks, roots, and trash are removed, row planters are usually used.

The most serious problem to be solved in broadcast or aerial seeding is that of getting good coverage and adequate seed-soil contact. A disk, a harrow and/or a cultipacker are the implements usually used to work the seed into the soil. Regardless of the implement used, some seed will be placed too deep, some too shallow, and some without good soil contact. Nonuniform emergence and stands will be the result.

Another problem is that of lodging. As soybeans are crowded together, they tend to grow taller and lodge more. Lodging is often severe in broadcast soybeans. This means the use of a lodging resistant variety is very important if soybeans are to be broadcast seeded.

Soybeans as a Green Manure Crop

Soybeans may be used as a green manure crop. The nitrogen that is returned to the soil when the crop is plowed down will vary with plant size. The seed, leaves, pods, and stems of a 30-bushel-per-acre crop contain about 165 pounds of nitrogen. How much of this nitrogen originated from the soil and how much

is taken from the atmosphere by the soybean rhizobia depends on the nitrogen level of the soil and growing conditions. The estimate under most conditions ranges from one-half to two-thirds from the rhizobia. For the greatest benefit, plowing should be delayed until the soybeans have made their maximum growth. They may be turned under when green or after ripening.

Inoculation

The nitrogen-fixing bacteria (rhizobia) that live on soybean roots are not native to most soils. The best way to introduce the bacteria is to inoculate the seed. Once introduced, the rhizobia remain viable for a long time.

The rhizobia are unicellular, microscopic plants that invade the plant through its root hairs. Once established on the soybean root, the bacteria take gaseous nitrogen from the atmosphere and fix it in forms easily used by the soybean plant. In return, the plant provides nodules where the rhizobia can live and work. It also manufactures sugar which the rhizobia use for energy.

The soybean rhizobia living in the soil are as capable of invading the soybean roots as those provided in the inoculin on the seed. Therefore, the value of inoculating seed to be planted on fields with long histories of soybean production is often questioned. Research and extension workers in seven out of 19 states surveyed recommend inoculating seed every

year, regardless of the cropping history. Those in the remaining 12 generally agree that inoculation is not necessary as a regular practice in fields that have grown a crop of well-nodulated soybeans within the past three to five years.

Workers in all states agree that inoculation is necessary on land where soybeans have not been grown or where the interval between soybean crops has been many years.

Research has demonstrated that there are many strains of soybean rhizobia. These vary in their nitrogen-fixing ability. The difference in effectiveness can be demonstrated relatively easily in the laboratory or in soil that contains no other soybean rhizobia. Demonstrating superior effectiveness under field conditions is more difficult. In soils well supplied with soybean rhizobia, those introduced with the seed usually account for only a small percent of the nodules formed. In such a case, the majority of the nodules result from rhizobia already in the soil.

The effectiveness of inoculating seed can be tested by planting inoculated and noninoculated seed in alternating strips. At least two strips of each should be planted in a part of the field free from dead furrows, low spots, or other characteristics that might have an effect on one strip and not the others.

Where inoculation is used, the actual mixing of the inoculin with the seed should be done carefully. The most effective on-farm treatment is a slurry of inoculin and one-half pint of water per bushel of seed applied

from several hours to one day before planting. The seed should be dry, however, before planting. More common is the practice of placing alternate layers of seed and inoculin in the seed hopper at planting time. Custom inoculation is done by some midwestern elevators at the time planting seed is cleaned. Seed should be planted soon after inoculation.

Growth Regulators

In an effort to improve yields, researchers have tested the effect of many chemical compounds on the soybean plant. These materials collectively are commonly referred to as growth regulators. When applied to the seed or plant, they change the normal growth or reproductive processes.

These materials can be used to improve lodging resistance, attain higher positioning of the lowest pods, and reduce the number of flowers shed. Plant breeders also have explored the possibility of inducing self-sterility with a growth regulator. This could not only reduce the tediousness of making crosses, but might be a valuable step in the development of commercial hybrids. One growth regulator, 2,3,5-triiodobenzoic acid (TIBA), is being marketed as Regim-8.

Foliar application of TIBA shortens the plant, increases branching, and shortens the leaf petioles. In the upper part of the plant, the petioles tend to be more vertically oriented. The net result is a change in plant shape from what might be described as a

bush to a cone. Lodging resistance is improved. The number of pods set is increased when TIBA is applied at the onset of flowering. Seed size is usually decreased. After Regim-8 had been used by soybean growers for two years, a survey indicated that yields were increased by one to 12 bushels per acre in 75 percent of the cases where applications were made according to recommendations. In the remaining cases, yields were decreased by one to six bushels per acre. The average yield increase under field conditions is about 10 percent.

Most of the experimental work with TIBA has been in the Corn Belt where soybeans respond to narrow rows. The use of narrow rows is even more essential when TIBA is applied because of its effect on plant height. Narrow rows, relatively high population, high fertility, and a full-season variety appear to be necessary for best results with TIBA.

Soybeans on Newly Cleared Land

A new, specialized type of soybean farming was developed during the 1960's. It was in this decade that land reclamation and land clearing in the Midsouth, the southeast and along the east coast opened hundreds of thousands of acres for soybean production. For this activity, midsoutherners coined the term, *new ground farming,* which became a familiar part of the agricultural jargon.

This activity has at least three implications to the overall soybean industry. First, it contributes a large volume of soybeans to the market. Second, some techniques and principles required in this type of farming are equally adapted on well-established farms where fencerows and small woodlots are cleared for more efficient use of high-capacity equipment. Third, a new breed of soybean grower and philosophy of soybean production have evolved from this activity.

The soybean grower operating on newly cleared land abides by a unique production system. His way of life is one of vast acreages, heavy-duty equipment, innumerable breakdowns and constant companionship with the portable welding rig.

Land clearing may be done by contractors or by the grower himself, if the operation is of a size that merits ownership of the heavy-duty, expensive equipment required for this work. Clearing is done whenever the weather permits, but, for the most part, is concentrated in the period from June through December. Five to eight days after the green trees are piled, they are ignited and burned. Then the piles are broken and the unburned material is repiled and ignited again.

Meanwhile, stumps and smaller debris, such as chunks and limbs, must be removed from the land. This material must be removed for efficient use of planters, cultivators and combines.

When the land is cleared, it must be smoothed. This is done to various degrees by land-moving scoops, land planes and heavy-duty disks.

Finally, when the land appears to be approaching a productive state, another important task remains to

30. Soybeans treated with the growth regulator TIBA have crinkled, thickened leaves. Use of the chemical at the onset of flowering increases pod set and yield.

be done. This is the critical job of drainage. Very often, the land being cleared is of a low, swampy nature. This is the reason much of it has remained uncultivated for so long. Therefore, it is imperative that an extensive ditching system be constructed to remove water and prevent ponding. This job is equally important in the new-ground operations of the Midsouth and the land reclamation projects along the east coast, where fields are no more than 5 to 20 feet above sea level. Many planting companies undertaking extensive land-clearing projects employ consulting agricultural engineers or retired Soil Conservation Service engineers to supervise the drainage work.

Liming Is Important

Low soil pH is one of the first problems to be solved. Newly cleared land in the Midsouth and southeast nearly always is acid. Many fields in the delta originally have a pH of 5.5 to 5.0. Since soybeans will not grow well at these levels, it is agronomically important that lime be applied before the first crop is planted. Three tons of lime per acre may cost as much as $18, applied, but the productive potential is increased enough to make this worthwhile. In such cases, extension specialists stick to their recommendation that lime should be used anytime the pH is below 6.0.

On some operations, however, where the only enterprise is new-ground soybeans, managers take a different view. They reason that the purchase and clearing of land require extensive capital outlay, and

that soil improvements must be delayed for two or more years. To the grower operating newly cleared land, the problem of coming up with an additional $18 per acre may be greater than it seems in print or conversation. Economically, then, there may be room for argument about the decision; agronomically, there is a clear-cut case in favor of lime from the beginning.

If possible, lime should be broadcast and disked in during the fall. This will allow for some correction of soil pH before the soybean crop is up and growing the following summer.

Even when lime is applied, it usually pays to apply molybdenum, a micronutrient that is relatively unavailable at low pH. Many new-ground soybean growers routinely use planting seed treated with sodium molybdate.

Also of major importance is the inoculation of planting seed. On newly cleared soil, there is no reason to expect nodulating bacteria to be present. There is little question from most growers about the economics of inoculating soybean seed on new ground. Recommended rates of inoculant should be used in all cases. Seed treated before planting time should be kept out of direct sunlight and high temperatures.

It is impossible to generalize on the fertility status of newly cleared soybean land. Phosphorus is often deficient on new ground in the coastal plain area of south Mississippi. Potassium deficiency is an infrequent problem in this area, but sometimes crops up as a major deficiency elsewhere.

Nitrogen Often Used

Some growers routinely apply nitrogen on new ground before planting soybeans. They broadcast and disk in about 30 pounds of nitrogen per acre to assure that adequate amounts of the nutrient are available until nodulation provides the plants' needs. In the case of newly cleared land, the best suggestion is to take soil samples intensively and fertilize according to recommendations.

Soil preparation is held to a minimum on most newly cleared land, for the simple reason that stumps and debris complicate tillage operations. It is an unspoken rule in many quarters that every implement should be of the spring-trip type, if possible, in order to minimize the damage that occurs from hanging machinery in buried stumps and chunks of wood.

The planting method varies. If the field debris is removed, many growers prefer to plant soybeans in rows. Row planting allows the use of a cultivator. Even in the lower South, where narrow rows have not shown any particular yield advantage, new-ground soybeans sometimes are planted in 30-inch rows to provide quick shading of the soil as a weed control measure.

Broadcast planting is preferred by some growers because of the damage that results if planters are used in debris-clogged fields. Seed with 90 percent germination should be broadcast with an end-gate seeder, bulk fertilizer spreader or airplane at a rate of about 75 pounds per acre. If the germination is higher or lower, the rate should be adjusted. The seed should be disked into the soil, with the disks cutting to a depth twice as great as the desired seed placement.

Overplanting and irregular distribution may cause lodging in broadcast plantings. Seeding rates of 90 pounds per acre or more can result in thick populations of plants that lodge, particularly on rich soil that tends to produce rank growth.

The choice of variety may be critical in planting soybeans on newly cleared land. It is advisable to use a variety that sets its lowest pods several inches above the soil surface. This will make it possible to raise the cutterbar above the field debris at combining time without sacrificing yield. Two southern varieties, Semmes and Bragg, were popular for use on new ground in the late 1960's and early 1970's. These varieties not only set their lowest pods relatively high, but they also produce dense shade.

Generally, weeds are not a severe problem the first few years land is cleared out of dense woods. Most weeds do not grow well in the shade of heavy forest. For this reason, many growers do not use herbicides at first. This does not mean they can relax, however. If a swamp or forest is broken by small clearings, as is the case in some regions, the grower should assume that those clearings will offer a residue of weed seed to infest the remainder of his land.

Wood Ash Presents Problems

Grower experience shows that most pre-emergence

herbicides are rendered ineffective by large concentrations of wood ash in the soil. Because of this, many new-ground farmers vigorously disk and re-disk burning sites to spread the ash deposits. If they fail to do so, those sites may indeed be the first to become weedy.

The man who broadcasts his planting seed forfeits the option to cultivate new-ground soybeans. His only hope will be a carefully chosen, aerially applied post-emergence herbicide. In such cases, particularly for control of cocklebur, 2,4-DB has been used to good advantage. The grower who plants in rows may rely on his cultivator, as well as directed postemergence herbicides. Even if he uses spring-trip cultivators, he will find it critically important to keep a portable welding rig nearby for making quick repairs.

Harvesting soybeans on newly cleared land is an experience to make most combine operators shudder. Debris picked up by the combine can damage the header auger, the finger feeders and the cylinder.

Regarding yield, here is a consensus of growers experienced in producing new-ground soybeans in the delta, the southern coastal plain and the east coast of the Carolinas and Virginia: During the first year, new-ground soybeans will yield about 75 to 85 percent as much as those in a similar soil that has been cultivated extensively. During the second year, yields will increase somewhat. By the third to fourth year, yields will equal those of soybeans on a similar field that has been cultivated over a period of years.

Yields may actually exceed those on well-established fields by 15 to 20 percent for several years.

Under the warm, humid conditions that prevail in most areas where land clearing is occurring, the debris decays within three to five years. After this, the soil is no longer considered new ground, but is an established field.

31

4

Fertilizer for Soybeans

There is much misunderstanding about fertilizing soybeans. But the results of widespread soybean fertilization research are remarkably consistent. Soybeans respond very well to fertilizer when soil test values are low in the South and on deep, dark-colored Corn Belt soils.

The soil test readings that are ideal for corn in terms of pH, phosphorus, and potassium are also ideal for soybeans. There are three main differences in fertilizing the two crops. Corn requires large amounts of nitrogen, soybeans seldom need any. The use of row fertilizer is safer, and often more effective, with corn. And micronutrient requirements of the two crops are different.

The Essential Elements

Most crops require the same elements, but in different proportions. The elements are grouped into major, secondary, and micronutrients (also called minor or trace elements—misleading terms because they suggest minor importance).

Nitrogen

Soybeans contain large amounts of nitrogen. In four to five months a 50-bushel-per-acre crop must get 295 pounds of nitrogen for vegetative growth and seed. It is generally accepted that well-nodulated soybeans can get enough nitrogen for yields of 30 to 40 bushels without fertilizer nitrogen. But what about yields of 50, 60, or even 100 bushels per acre? Can the nodules supply enough nitrogen for such high yields, especially during the pod-filling period? And what about young seedlings before the nodules form? Would deep-placed nitrogen be effective? Researchers are looking into these areas.

On dark-colored midwestern soils, nitrogen seldom if ever produces a profitable response on well-nodulated soybeans. In most cases, the increase is less than two bushels per acre and often it is zero. Nitrogen fertilizer is, therefore, not suggested by most midwestern agronomists, although a few recommend 5 to 10 pounds per acre in a mixed fertilizer near the row (not in contact with the seed) for insurance until the nodules form.

In the southern states, where most soils (except those in the delta) are notoriously low in nitrogen, agronomists say: "Experiments comparing nitrogen rates for soybean production have shown no yield increase for nitrogen fertilization." (B. L. Arnold, Mississippi)

"Soybeans, like other legumes, have the ability to supply their own nitrogen needs, provided they have been inoculated and the soil contains sufficient lime and other fertilizer elements. Therefore, it is not necessary to supply nitrogen fertilizer except possibly a small amount as a starter." (J. R. Johnson, Dr. J. E. Jackson, Dr. W. H. Gurley, Georgia)

"We have not found any consistent responses to nitrogen used on soybeans." (Dr. J. V. Baird, North Carolina)

Elemental and oxide expression of P and K

phosphorus

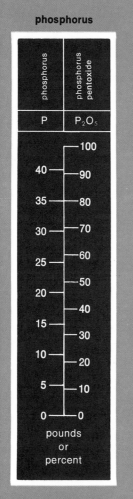

potassium

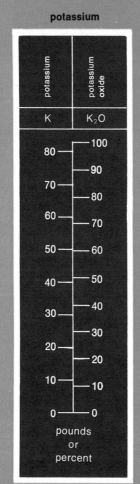

The 16
Essential Elements
for
Plant Growth

From fertilizer

Major (primary) nutrients

Nitrogen N

Phosphorus P

Potassium K

Secondary nutrients

Calcium Ca

Magnesium Mg

Sulfur S

Micronutrients

Boron B

Chlorine Cl

Copper Cu

Iron Fe

Manganese Mn

Molybdenum Mo

Zinc Zn

From air and water

Carbon C

Hydrogen H

Oxygen O

1

1. The words "grade" and "analysis" are used interchangeably to denote percentage of guaranteed plant nutrients. There are two currently-used ways of expressing these percentages. They may be put in terms of oxides of phosphorus and potassium, as has been the custom over many years, or they may be expressed in terms of the elements. A 6-24-24 fertilizer in oxide terms is a 6-10.5-19.9 fertilizer in elemental terms. At some future date fertilizer labels and reference materials will likely convert exclusively to the elemental terms. The conversion scales above and the following factors may be used in interpreting from one expression to the other.

percent or pounds of P x 2.29 equals P_2O_5

percent or pounds of P_2O_5 x 0.44 equals P

percent or pounds of K x 1.2 equals K_2O

percent or pounds of K_2O x 0.83 equals K

2. The belief that soybeans do not use much plant food is untrue, but widespread. The figures show major plant food content of soybean crops yielding 50 and 100 bushels per acre. At harvest, the beans contain about 75 percent of the nitrogen and phosphorus, and about 60 percent of the potassium, taken up by the plant during the season.

The soybean is a big user of N, P and K

2

50 bushels	100 bushels
295 pounds of nitrogen	560 pounds of nitrogen
25 pounds of phosphorus	48 pounds of phosphorus
105 pounds of potassium	200 pounds of potassium

"Under favorable conditions, nodules may form within a week after the seed sprout. But nitrogen fixation seems to be delayed until about two weeks later. For this reason, a temporary vegetative response to applied nitrogen is often observed on a nitrogen-deficient soil. But when nitrogen fixation goes into full swing, the plants usually seem to overcome the temporary deficiency." (Dr. Woody N. Miley, Arkansas)

Ten to 20 pounds of starter nitrogen in the mixed fertilizer placed 3 to 5 inches from the row is more likely to pay where soybeans have not been grown regularly, and on light-colored, low-organic matter soils in the South, than on dark soils. But irregardless of the soil type, if it tests high in phosphorus and potassium and the pH is above 6.0 so the nodulating bacteria grow well, applied nitrogen will produce only small increases on well-nodulated soybeans.

One reason for the poor nitrogen response is that the nodules become lazy when nitrogen is applied in the nodule-forming zone before planting. In other words, the harder a grower tries to increase yields with nitrogen fertilizer, the less nitrogen the nodules fix from the air. A natural question is whether an increase from nitrogen could be obtained if the depressing effect on nodules could be avoided.

To learn whether yields would be increased by nitrogen applied after the nodules had formed, researchers at the University of Illinois made sidedress applications of 100 and 200 pounds per acre at the early flowering and pod-filling stages. There was no consistently profitable gain.

In two other tests it appeared that small profits might be gained from delayed application of low-cost nitrogen:
— At the Pontotoc Ridge Branch Experiment Station in Mississippi, 100 pounds of nitrogen applied as a urea-ammonium nitrate solution at blooming time increased yield an average of 4.4 bushels per acre.
— In Ohio experiments, 100 pounds of nitrogen applied at flowering time increased yield 5.4 bushels per acre.

In both of these tests, however, the maximum yield was just 38 bushels per acre. This relatively low level of production indicates that poor nodulation or some other factor depressed yield. Responses to nitrogen might have been less if other limiting factors had been removed.

Another attempt dealt with the use of different rates of nitrogen on crops preceding soybeans. Experiments for two years at three locations in the Midwest showed an increase of only 1.5 bushels of soybeans per acre for 320 pounds of nitrogen applied for the previous crop.

Other attempts to supply nitrogen in ways that would not affect nodulation include deep placement (so the roots would not reach the nitrogen until mid-season) and subirrigation with a nutrient solution. Thus far, this research has not produced promising results.

3

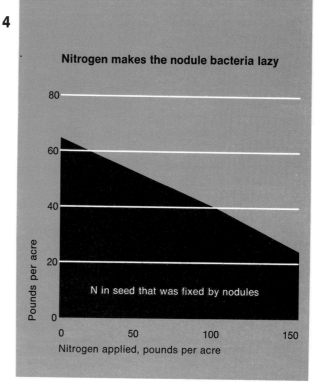

4

Nitrogen makes the nodule bacteria lazy

N in seed that was fixed by nodules

Pounds per acre

Nitrogen applied, pounds per acre

In summary, research agronomists have been frustrated in their attempts to produce substantial yield increases by applying nitrogen to well-nodulated soybeans.

Other Nitrogen-Using Approaches

Substituting nitrogen for nodules: Since nodule growth and nitrogen fixation require plant energy, some persons have suggested that a non-nodulating soybean, heavily fertilized with nitrogen, might out-yield the normal type. Some data suggests that this is possible, but that the rate of nitrogen would have to be in excess of 200 pounds per acre. It should be noted, however, that in greenhouse studies an Ohio researcher was unable to obtain maximum yield of soybeans without nodules although plenty of nitrogen was added; or with nodules, unless some nitrogen was added.

Increasing nodulation: If nitrogen is the limiting factor at high yield levels, could the presence of more nodules increase yield? Since available nitrogen depresses nodule formation, researchers reasoned that a shortage of nitrogen might increase the number of nodules. Iowa researcher Dr. C. R. Weber added 20 tons of corncobs per acre to reduce the supply of available nitrogen in the soil. The amount of nitrogen fixed by nodule bacteria was raised 67 percent in nondrouth seasons, but final yield was unchanged. Similarly, propane greatly increased the number of nodules in Iowa greenhouse studies, but has not in-

3. Soybean fertility research is full of surprises. The plant on the right, which received phosphorus and potassium, but no nitrogen, is as thrifty as those that received all three nutrients. The center plant, which received 200 pounds of nitrogen, has nodules but the one to its left, which received 400 pounds of nitrogen, has none. At this stage of growth, however, the plant receiving 400 pounds of nitrogen has the most vigorous root system. The plant receiving the heaviest rate of fertilizer nearly died in midseason.

4. As the nitrogen fertilization rate was increased, the nitrogen in the seed coming from nodule fixation declined. The data was taken over a period of four nondrouth years by C. R. Weber, Iowa State University.

creased soybean yields in university field tests.

Foliar application: Spraying nitrogen on soybean leaves at the time of peak need would appear to be a logical way to supplement the soil supply without affecting nodulation. Only a few research trials have been conducted but the results have not been encouraging.

Phosphorus

Soybeans require relatively large amounts of phosphorus. The seed and vegetative parts of a crop yielding 50 bushels per acre contain 25 pounds of phosphorus, compared to 11 pounds for a 50-bushel wheat crop and 40 pounds for a 150-bushel corn crop. There is no specific phosphorus deficiency symptom on soybeans, so soil tests are the only reliable fertilization guide.

Phosphorus is taken up by soybeans throughout

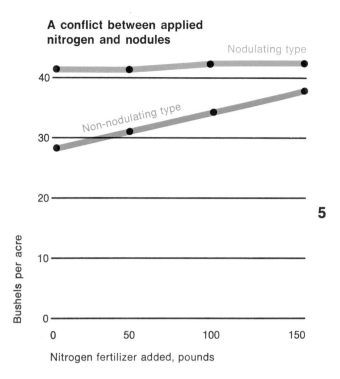

A conflict between applied nitrogen and nodules

Nodulating type

Non-nodulating type

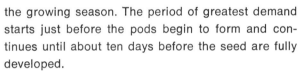

Bushels per acre

40

30

20

10

0

0   50   100   150

Nitrogen fertilizer added, pounds

5

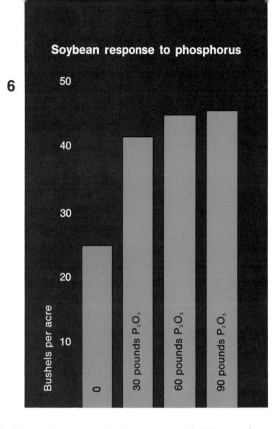

Soybean response to phosphorus

6

50

40

30

20

10

Bushels per acre

0

30 pounds P₂O₅

60 pounds P₂O₅

90 pounds P₂O₅

the growing season. The period of greatest demand starts just before the pods begin to form and continues until about ten days before the seed are fully developed.

Phosphorus stress on most plants occurs in the seedling stage, mainly because the size and feeding capacity of the root system are not yet balanced to the phosphorus needs. Besides, the soil is more likely to be cool and wet in the spring, reducing phosphorus uptake. However, soybeans do not get the early growth stimulation from a small amount of phosphorus placed near the seed that is usually seen on corn. This may be because soybeans are more sensitive to fertilizer "burn", hence, any stimulation from extra phosphorus might be cancelled out by the salt effect.

Because phosphorus is taken up throughout the season, it should be mixed through the plow layer rather than concentrated near the surface. The top few inches of soil may become so dry that roots cannot feed effectively.

Much of the phosphorus used by soybean plants is taken up, then later translocated from leaves, stems, and petioles into the seed. This relieves the root system from part of its job of taking up phosphorus late in the season. This is fortunate, because root growth slows markedly after seed begin to develop and thus the capacity to take up phosphorus, which depends upon continued root extension, slows down.

5. In the study represented here, non-nodulating soybeans responded well to nitrogen fertilizer, but nodulating soybeans did not. There are indications that the non-nodulating variety would have equalled the nodulating type at a nitrogen fertilization rate of about 200 pounds per acre in this experiment at Iowa State University.

6. This graph represents an excellent response to phosphorus. The trial was conducted on a deep, dark soil testing very low in phosphorus, but adequate in pH and potassium.

If a large amount of the element is to be applied to a very low-testing soil at one time, it should be broadcast and plowed down. The phosphorus will be mixed through 6 to 12 inches of soil, and thus will be available if midsummer drouth prevents uptake of the nutrient from the top few inches. Except in dry periods, phosphorus that is broadcast and disked into the surface is quite effective.

Mixing phosphorus fertilizer into the soil is important because this element moves in the soil the least of any major nutrient. Within a few hours to a few days after application, some of the soluble phosphorus may move as much as an inch from the granule, but it moves hardly at all thereafter. Long-term experiments reveal little increase in available phosphorus at the 18-inch depth after 50 years of fertilizing the plow layer. This tie-up of phosphorus has several important implications:

— So-called "fixed" phosphorus is much less available than freshly applied phosphorus. A grower must apply more than is removed in his harvested

7. When a phosphorus granule is placed in the soil it attracts moisture and begins to dissolve. The resulting strongly acid solution reacts with iron, aluminum, manganese, potassium, and calcium compounds. About one third of the phosphorus remains at the granule site, but it too has changed chemically and little is still soluble. All phosphate fertilizers soon change chemically in the soil. The nature of change depends on the compound added and the kind of soil. Captions below pictures at the right give a running narration of the reactions of fertilizer phosphorus in the soil.

A. After one half hour in the soil: Moisture is gathering around the fertilizer granule. This particular granule contained potassium chloride, to hasten water absorption.

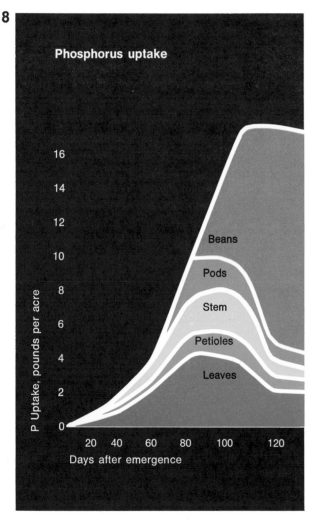

8. Soybeans continue to take up phosphorus until the beans are almost mature, as shown in Iowa State University tests.

crops.

— Since phosphorus moves very little, feeding roots must penetrate into new zones of available phosphorus continuously if plants are to make the best growth.

— Crops get only 5 to 20 percent of their phosphorus from fertilizer in the year in which it is applied. One reason for this is that only a small part of the root system is in contact with the freshly applied fertilizer throughout most of the growing season.

— Subsoil levels can be raised very little because phosphorus applied to the plow layer stays near where it is placed.

— The total phosphorus in the plow layer can be raised to a high level easily. A recent survey in Illinois showed that about one-third of the fields growing soybeans or corn had been built as high as necessary for top profit. Only maintenance applications will be needed in the future.

Phosphorus Fertilizers

Phosphate rock is the source of phosphorus for fertilizer. The phosphorus in naturally occurring rock slowly will become available in acid soils. For quick release the rock must be treated with acid or heat in order to free 90 percent of the phosphorus so it can be absorbed by plant roots.

Ordinary or orthophosphoric acid can be made by either of two processes. Phosphate rock can be heated in an electric furnace to produce elemental

B. After 30 hours in the soil: Movement of strongly acid solution is nearing its maximum spread. About one fifth of the chemically changed phosphorus remains in the original zone.

C. After five days in the soil: Reactions are essentially complete. The phosphorus is now in new compounds varying in degrees of availability. Movement has been 1 to 1½ inches.

phosphorus which is burned to P_2O_5 and then reacted with water. The product is called white or furnace acid. The rock also can be treated with sulfuric acid, followed by processes which separate out the gypsum and concentrate the liquid acid by evaporation. The products, containing from 30.5 percent phosphorus (furnace acid) to 31.4 percent (wet process), can be applied directly as liquid phosphoric acid; can be used to treat phosphate rock to make triple-superphosphate; can be combined with ammonia into ammonium phosphates; can be used in liquid mixed fertilizers; or can be concentrated into superphosphoric acid through evaporation.

Superphosphoric acid contains phosphorus in two broad categories: ordinary orthophosphate and polyphosphate. When the acid contains up to about 29.6 percent phosphorus, the element is in the usual orthophosphate form. When placed in the soil, orthophosphate quickly enters into reactions and the phosphorus becomes less available than it was in the fertilizer. Acid containing from 29.6 to 36.2 percent phosphorus (the maximum) has about half of the phosphorus in the form of polyphosphates. These forms of the element are credited by some fertilizer men with making the phosphorus more available and somewhat more mobile, and with helping to release micronutrients from the soil. Polyphosphates do not enter directly into the soil reactions, but must first take on one or more molecules of water and be converted back to the usable orthophosphate.

In spite of extravagant claims, field trials show few consistent differences between polyphosphates and orthophosphate in ability to supply phosphorus. This should be expected for at least three reasons. First, polyphosphate fertilizers usually contain about one-half of the phosphorus in the ortho form (the proportion may change in the future). Second, only 5 to 20 percent of the phosphorus used by a crop is obtained from the fertilizer applied that year. Third, the theoretical advantage of less reaction with the soil may be offset by the fact that polyphosphate is not available to the plant until it converts back to orthophosphate.

Regarding the effect of polyphosphates on micronutrient availability, research has shown that polyphosphates do not free enough micronutrient from the native soil supply to correct a severe deficiency. Also, polyphosphate accentuates zinc deficiency on corn more than does orthophosphate. When zinc is added to both phosphate forms, the yield increase is the same.

Recent research by the Tennessee Valley Authority indicates that polyphosphates do not move any more, if as much, as orthophosphates. The advantages of polyphosphates are that they permit the formulation of higher analysis liquid or suspension fertilizers without salting out; they keep three micronutrients (iron, zinc, manganese) in more available form; they save labor and cost in transporting because they permit higher analysis mixes.

How soil pH affects availability of phosphorus

	pH	Relative Availability	
Strongly alkaline	9.0	High	Phosphorus is partly in sodium compounds which are more available than calcium compounds.
Slightly alkaline	8.0	Low	Much of the phosphorus is in tricalcium phosphate which is low in availability. Tricalcium phosphate is like rock phosphate except that it has no flourine.
Neutral Slightly acid	7.0 6.0	High	Phosphorus compounds in this range are more available than in more acid or more alkaline soils.
Moderately acid Strongly acid	5.0 4.0	Low	In this range, much of the phosphorus is combined with iron, aluminum, and manganese into products of low availability.

Phosphorus Reactions in Soils

Phosphorus in the soil is most available in the pH range of 5.5 to 7.0. Because phosphorus is part of all living tissue, it is successively tied up and released as the crop grows, matures, and dies. When the residue is returned to the soil, the element is tied up in the body of microbes that cause the residues to decay. Most phosphorus eventually goes into the soil's storage reservoir.

Crop residues such as soybean stems and corn stalks are low in phosphorus. They temporarily depress the availability of phosphorus in the soil. The amount of available phosphorus is influenced by the inherent amount of phosphorus in the soil parent material, the pH of the surface and subsoil, and the amount of organic matter, which contains about half the total phosphorus in the soil. Also important are root depth and branching (a much-branched root system contacts the maximum available phosphorus), as well as subsoil structure (large, dense soil blocks in the subsoil limit the feeding surface).

Potassium

Soybeans require relatively large amounts of potassium. A crop of soybeans yielding 50 bushels per acre removes 105 pounds of potassium, while a 150-bushel corn crop removes only 33 pounds in the grain.

The rate of potassium uptake climbs to a peak during the period of rapid vegetative growth, then slows down about the time the beans begin to form. The uptake is completed two to three weeks before the seed matures. At maturity, soybean seed contain 60 percent of the potassium in the plant, whereas in corn the grain contains less than 25 percent of the plant's total.

Some potassium is moved from other parts of the soybean plant to the developing seed, but the amount is not as great as in the case of nitrogen and phosphorus. Alfalfa and clover are luxury consumers of potassium; that is, they take up far more than they need for maximum yield. Soybeans do not.

Generally, soybean growers can afford to raise the potassium content of their soils to a high level for several reasons. Potassium leaches very little, except on sands. It is not used in excess by soybeans. And it is the lowest cost nutrient used by soybeans.

Extension agronomists in the southern states have lower soil test goals for potassium than those in the midwestern states. Most, for example, indicate that at a potassium test of 150 there is little or no reason to make an application for soybeans. Midwestern agronomists, on the other hand, suggest that potassium fertilization is needed for soybeans at anything less than a test of 200, and some say 250.

When a soil has been built up to the desirable potassium level, the most profitable annual application rate on many soils is slightly less than the amount removed in harvested crops. This is because some potassium is released every year from the vast amount held in the soil in slowly available forms. This store-

9. The phosphorus cycle in the soil is due to chemical reactions, the working of soil organisms, and the growth of crops. The heavy arrows pointing downward indicate that phosphorus in the long term moves toward the large reservoir, from which only a small amount is released each year. From 25 to 60 percent of the phosphorus held in the reservoir is in organic compounds. The remainder is primarily in compounds involving calcium, iron, aluminum, and manganese.

Phosphorus reactions in the soil

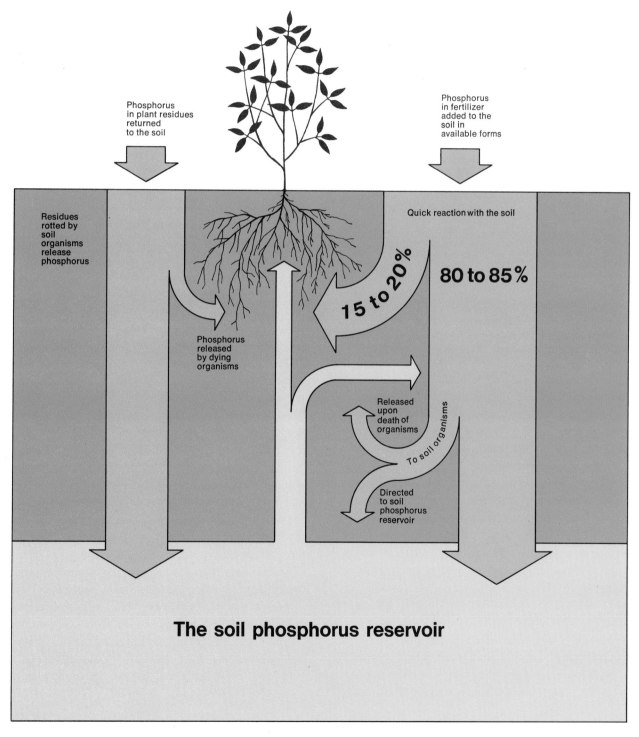

Phosphorus in plant residues returned to the soil

Phosphorus in fertilizer added to the soil in available forms

Residues rotted by soil organisms release phosphorus

Quick reaction with the soil

15 to 20%

80 to 85%

Phosphorus released by dying organisms

Released upon death of organisms

To soil organisms

Directed to soil phosphorus reservoir

The soil phosphorus reservoir

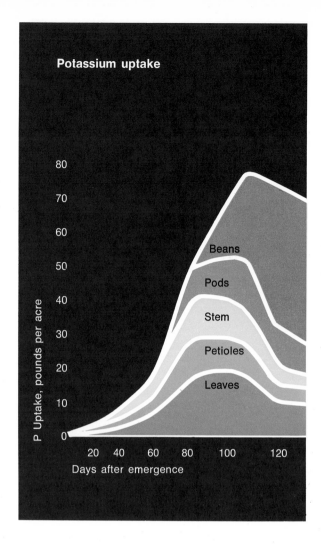

Potassium uptake

P Uptake, pounds per acre

80
70
60
50
40
30
20
10
0

Beans

Pods

Stem

Petioles

Leaves

20 40 60 80 100 120

Days after emergence

11. Potassium uptake is completed long before soybeans mature. During the final 20 days or more, potassium is transferred from plant vegetative parts to the seed, according to studies at Iowa State University.

house may contain 20,000 to 50,000 pounds per acre in each 6-inch layer. One exception to this is sandy soils which have little reserve potassium. Here, applications may need to exceed crop removal just to maintain a given soil test level.

As a rule, the heaviest drain on soil potassium is by crops from which the stalk and leaves are harvested, rather than the grain only. But among grain crops, the soybean is a heavy potassium user because the seed contain an unusually high amount of the element. One bushel of soybeans contains 1.15 pounds of potassium, compared to only .22 pound per bushel of shelled corn.

Potassium Reactions in Soils

Potassium differs from nitrogen and phosphorus in that it remains in solution in the sap of living plants. It is readily washed out of the tissues as soon as a leaf or whole plant dies. In fact, it washes out of dead

12. Soybean roots feed on the potassium in the soil solution, which is position 1. As the roots remove potassium, some exchangeable potassium moves from position 2 into position 1. Conversely, when potassium fertilizer is applied, the element goes into solution and then moves to position 2, provided the soil has adequate exchange capacity. Some fertilizer potassium moves to position 3. Potassium in position 4 is unavailable over a farmer's lifetime.

leaves even before they fall off the plant or are worked into the soil.

Potassium occurs in four distinct situations in soil, page 77. Potassium in the soil solution, position 1, is immediately available. As potassium is taken out of the soil solution by crop roots, more potassium moves from position 2 to replace it. When potassium fertilizer is added to the soil, it first goes into solution and then moves into position 2. In other words, potassium readily moves back and forth between positions 1 and 2. Position 2 is the place where potassium is held against loss by leaching, yet is readily available when needed.

Soils vary in the amount of potassium held in position 3. Although it does not show in the soil test, it occurs in some soils in large amounts which move slowly into position 2. This conversion occurs rapidly enough for the element in this position to be a significant source of potassium within a single growing season. Although there are some exceptions, soils in the northern states contain far more of the clays that hold potassium in positions 2 and 3 than do typical southern soils. This means that potassium fertilizer can be applied less frequently, but in larger amounts, to northern soils (except on sand which has a low potassium-holding power).

A point of considerable practical importance is that well-limed soils hold much more potassium in available form, positions 1 and 2, than do strongly acid soils.

Positions of potassium in the soil

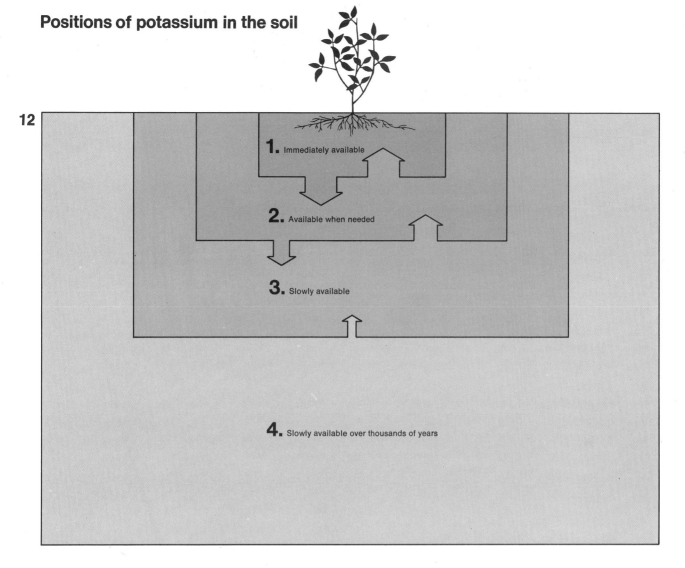

1. Immediately available

2. Available when needed

3. Slowly available

4. Slowly available over thousands of years

Soils very low in available potassium should be fertilized with this element in a series of applications rather than in a single, large treatment. Making one heavy application under such a condition will cause much of the element to go into position 3, where it is relatively unavailable. The low cost of fertilizer potassium, however, may make it more economical to ignore this fixation problem and apply a large amount, thus reducing application cost.

Soybeans take up potassium about equally well from row or broadcast placement. Most potassium fertilizers, however, have a high salt index, which means that they are likely to impair germination if placed close to the seed. Potassium for soybeans, if applied through the planter, should be placed two to five inches to the side and slightly below the seed.

In a soybeans-corn or soybeans-rice cropping system, the potassium may be applied ahead of either crop. If the element is applied ahead of corn, rice, or cotton, almost three-fourths of the amount will be returned to the soil in the crop residue. Since potassium is not tied up in structural tissues, it soon washes from these residues into the soil and is available for soybeans that follow. Soybeans do not suffer from feeding at the "second table," provided the table is full!

Potassium Fertilizers

Potassium fertilizers are relatively simple water-soluble salts. Since they have a high salt index, they must be kept at least 1½ and preferably 2 inches, from germinating seed. The major potassium fertilizers are as follows:

Muriate of potash (potassium chloride). This represents 90 percent of the fertilizer potassium in the United States. It varies in color from red to white and in particle size from coarse granules to powder. Most muriate contains 60 to 62 percent K_2O (49.8 to 51.5 percent potassium), though a small amount of 50 percent K_2O product is sold. This fertilizer is entirely satisfactory for soybeans. It is nearly always the lowest cost source of potassium.

Potassium sulfate. This white salt contains 48 to 50 percent K_2O (39.8 to 41.5 percent potassium). It is low

13

The importance of potassium supplying power

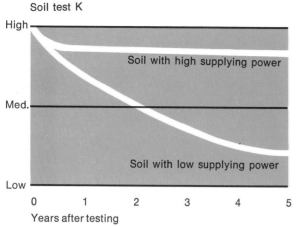

13. During the first year following an application of potassium fertilizer, different soils with the same test may supply nearly equal rates of the nutrient. But soils with a low potassium supplying power provide quickly declining amounts of the element in the following years. These soils require more frequent applications of potassium.

in chlorine content. Since it costs more than muriate, it has no advantage for use on soybeans unless sulfur is known to be deficient. Even in that case, buying potassium chloride and sulfur separately might be more economical.

Sulfate of potash-magnesia. This material contains 22 to 23 percent K_2O (18.3 to 19.2 percent potassium), 18 to 19 percent MgO (about 11 percent magnesium) and sulfur. It is an expensive source of potassium alone, but is economical and is extremely important for special crops and soils where all three nutrients —potassium, magnesium, and sulfur—are needed.

Potassium nitrate. This potassium fertilizer contains 13.8 percent nitrogen and up to 46.6 percent K_2O (38.7 percent potassium). It has no agronomic advantage over muriate where high chloride is not objectionable. It is well suited for use in liquid fertilizers because it is readily soluble.

Potassium metaphosphate. This extremely high analysis source of phosphorus and potassium—55 percent P_2O_5 (24 percent phosphorus) and 35 percent K_2O (29 percent potassium) — has been produced for nearly 30 years in a pilot plant for trial purposes but has not yet entered the commercial market.

Secondary Nutrients

Deficiencies of the three secondary nutrients—calcium, magnesium, and sulfur—are not nearly so common as in the case of the major nutrients. On a pound for pound basis, soybeans contain more of the sec-

14

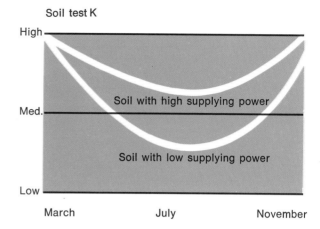

14. The supplying power of the soil must be considered in making an interpretation of soil test results. Tests on soil with a low natural supplying power for potassium drop sharply in midseason, while those on soils with a high supplying power undergo little change. It is important to consider the type of soil and month of sampling.

ondary nutrients than small grains and corn, except for sulfur in corn.

Calcium and Magnesium

Adequate amounts of calcium and magnesium are provided for many field crops by the limestone used to adjust soil pH. A deficiency of calcium for soybeans is unlikely if the pH is 6.0 or above. Except for the Coastal Plains of the Atlantic seaboard and gulf coast, there may be a few, but not many, soils deficient in magnesium at pH 6.0 or above.

A few soil testing laboratories have stirred up a lot of concern in the Midwest over calcium-magnesium balance. It is difficult to see how soils in this region could be out of balance naturally or thrown into imbalance by applications of limestone. The most common statement is that there is too much magnesium. Soils do not naturally contain as much magnesium as calcium and there is no limestone that contains more magnesium than calcium.

The magnesium uptake of some crops, including soybeans, can be reduced by large applications of potassium or the occurrence of a high level of potassium in the soil. But soybeans are not especially sensitive to magnesium deficiency. No research has been reported in which potassium reduced yields by causing a shortage of magnesium.

Sulfur

Sulfur deficiencies are limited to special soils, crops,

15. Micronutrients, needed in very small amounts, can produce spectacular results when used to correct deficiencies. Zinc chelate was used beside the row in the background.

and geographical areas. Few deficiencies have been reported for soybeans in the field. This may change for two reasons. First, improved manufacturing methods have reduced the amount of sulfur in fertilizers compared to the old fertilizers using ordinary 20 percent superphosphate as the main source of phosphorus. Second, air pollution control efforts are reducing the amount of sulfur exhausted in smoke and thus returned to the soil in rainfall.

Soil tests for sulfur are not of much value. The amount of sulfur that is available depends on the rate at which it is released from organic matter. The rate of release is influenced by the kind of residue and soil moisture, temperature, and soil pH. These conditions vary from field to field, and from year to year.

Micronutrients

Deficiencies of micronutrients (also called trace or minor elements) are more widespread on soybeans than on most field crops. Shortages of iron, manganese, molybdenum, and zinc have been found in some soybean fields in the United States.

Where a micronutrient deficiency is acute, the response to small, corrective applications is unbelievably striking. But more often the response, if any, is only a few bushels per acre.

For this reason, it is often difficult for growers to get reliable results from field strip trials with micronutrients.

The margin between too little, just enough, and too

79

16. These fertilizer pellets have been spray-coated with micronutrients, assuring uniform field application and preventing separation of ingredients. The pellets, shown much larger than actual size, are about 8 mesh, or a maximum dimension of about 0.093 inch. The acidity that develops around fertilizer pellets in the soil helps to reduce the fixation of certain nutrients when the pH is high.

much of a micronutrient is narrow in many cases. Different varieties of the same crop, especially soybeans, respond differently to certain nutrients.

Soil tests have thus far not been nearly so satisfactory for determining micronutrient deficiencies as have plant analyses. The use of the spectrograph has helped tremendously to identify micronutrient problems and to learn how to solve them.

Serious micronutrient deficiencies in the United States are limited mainly to the following:

— Strongly weathered soils. These soils are old in terms of the extent of chemical and physical changes that have occurred. Many have lost nutrients in the soybean rooting zone through leaching. Soils in the southeastern and gulf coast states are more leached than those in the northern states because many are coarse-textured, rainfall is higher, and leaching occurs the year-round.

— Coarse-textured soils. These soils were formed from rock materials low in micronutrients. Furthermore, rainfall penetrates coarse soils much more rapidly, and to a greater depth, and causes more leaching of nutrients from sandy and gravelly soils than from loams, silt loams, and silty clay loams.

— Alkaline soils. The solubility, though not total supply, of several nutrients goes down as pH goes up. However, it is not feasible to lower the pH of alkaline soils to correct micronutrient deficiencies of soybeans.

— Organic soils. These soils have a low mineral con-

tent. Some of the most serious manganese and iron deficiencies are on high pH organic soils.

The first farmers to experience micronutrient deficiencies may be the best in their communities. They are the ones who have supplied plenty of nitrogen, phosphorus, and potassium and raised yields to the point where stress is put on the micronutrients. Growers obtaining average yields should not try micronutrient applications unless deficiencies have been proven to exist on their soil type. Other practices should get first attention.

Prevent or Cure Deficiencies?

Where micronutrient deficiencies are not yet reported, there are two points of view on making applications. One side argues that it is best to apply small amounts regularly as a preventive. Growers taking this view may simply use premium grades of fertilizer which contain micronutrients, as well as secondary nutrients. The other side advocates waiting until specific deficiencies occur, then correcting them.

Members of the first group, the "preventers," usually apply small amounts of a complex mixture of several nutrients in the row or broadcast. Micronutrients applied in this way are, at best, partial insurance against slight deficiencies. There are several arguments against this approach. The insurance value may fail to cover the added cost of applying nutrients that are not deficient now nor expected to be in the foreseeable future. If the fertilizer is broadcast

17. The varietal difference in response to iron is shown in this field where both rows were fertilized identically. The Wayne variety, right, either has a higher iron requirement or a lower capability to take up and use iron, than the variety on the left. Soil pH was 8.2.

on high pH soil where deficiencies are most likely, some nutrients will soon become unavailable.

The other group that waits to detect specific deficiencies has three sound reasons for its approach. A complex mixture seldom contains enough of an element to correct a serious deficiency. Also a combination of three to five nutrients often adds $5 to $10 to the price of a ton of fertilizer. And finally, the best method of applying one micronutrient can differ from that of another.

Chelates

Some micronutrients are available in organic ring compounds that hold the nutrient against soil fixation. These are called chelates. Iron and zinc have been chelated more than other micronutrients for field crops, but formulations of copper and manganese are also available.

Chelates are higher priced than other forms of the nutrients, but fewer pounds are needed to correct a deficiency. The use of chelates on soybeans is so new that each grower should check with his county agent, state college of agriculture, or fertilizer dealer on recommendations and current developments. Since chelates sometimes are very toxic to seedlings, the manufacturers' instructions must be followed.

Chelates are used mainly for soil application, but may also be used as foliar treatments. Any grower planning to test foliar application of a chelate can easily check the safe concentration. This is the pro-cedure: Mix up a small amount, for example a cupful, of a concentrated solution and dip one soybean leaf in it. Transfer the solution to a larger container, add another cup of water and dip a second leaf. Continue until 5 to 10 leaves are treated with increasing dilution. Keep a record of the concentration put on each leaf. Watch the leaves for several days. Select the treatment that is one or two dilutions below that which caused visible injury.

Fritts

Fritts are finely ground bits of glass to which micronutrients are added while in the molten state. Because they dissolve slowly, a single application lasts several years, whereas more soluble forms are used up, leached out, or made unavailable by soil reaction. There has been little research on fritts as a source of micronutrients for soybeans.

Boron

No boron deficiency has been found on soybeans in the field. In fact, Ohio agronomists are more concerned with too much than too little boron in soybeans and corn. This element is least available in strongly acid and alkaline soils.

Boron is extremely toxic to young seedlings and consequently should not be mixed into a band fertilizer for soybeans even on a trial basis. If a test application is made, it should be broadcast and worked into the seedbed at a rate of 2½ pounds of actual

boron (25 pounds of borax or equivalent in other formulations) per acre. The range between too little and too much is narrower than for any other micronutrient.

Copper

Purdue agronomists reported promising results with copper treatments on soybeans on widely scattered Indiana soils in 1967 and 1968.

North Carolina researchers reported a response to copper on mineral soil with 15 to 25 percent organic matter and a pH near 6.0. Such soil occupies a very small acreage. No plant deficiency symptom showed, hence the deficiency affected only seed yield. Others have reported shortages in sensitive crops on acid, highly leached sandy soils, and on calcareous (free limestone) soils. On sensitive crops, copper shortage is usually associated with high organic matter which ties up copper in unavailable form.

North Carolina agronomists suggest an application of 10 to 20 pounds of copper sulfate mixed through the soil, or one-half this in the fertilizer band.

If the chelated form is used, 1½ pounds of 13 percent formulation should be dissolved in 100 gallons of water and used to wet the foliage thoroughly. One early season application will likely be enough. Few states make soil tests for copper. Michigan State University makes a copper test on organic soils only. Possible shortages can best be determined by plant analysis or field trials.

Iron

Iron deficiency is the second most-frequent micronutrient deficit of soybeans in the Corn Belt, although molybdenum ranks second in southern states. (Manganese deficiency is the most common micronutrient problem in both areas.)

Deficiencies are limited to high pH soils, usually well above pH 7.0. This is because high pH produces the ferric form of iron which is unavailable. Other soil factors that cause iron deficiency are high calcium or magnesium carbonate and excess phosphorus, copper, manganese, and zinc. Some agronomists believe that the manganese-to-iron ratio in plants should be 1.5 to 2.5.

Wet soil, unusually low or high temperature, and intense sunlight make iron deficiency worse. Where a deficiency is only moderate, soybeans often outgrow the early deficiency symptoms, but yield is likely to be reduced. In marginal situations, some varieties are extremely stunted and yellow whereas others are normal.

Since iron shortage is due to soil fixation, application of soluble salts to the soil does not correct the trouble. Several sources of iron chelates may be used according to directions of the manufacturer. Some chelates are formulated especially for acid soils, others for those high in pH.

Foliar sprays of iron have, until recently, been thought to be highly effective. But in 1969, both Iowa and Minnesota agronomists reported that no satisfac-

Molybdenum need is greatest on acid soil

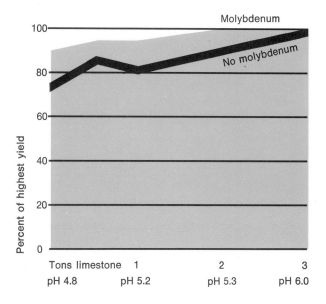

Percent of highest yield

Molybdenum

No molybdenum

Tons limestone	1	2	3
pH 4.8	pH 5.2	pH 5.3	pH 6.0

18. Soybeans growing on acid soil have the greatest need for molybdenum. It is at the lowest indicated pH level at the left side of the chart that the spread is greatest between yields of soybeans with and without molybdenum. The spread gradually declines until, at pH 6.0, there is no response to added molybdenum. The study was conducted at Mississippi's Brown Loam Branch Experiment Station.

tory way had been found to correct iron deficiency. A one-half to one percent ferric sulfate spray used heavily enough to wet the leaves thoroughly is suggested for trial use. Each new crop of leaves needs spraying (two or three sprays per season) until changes in the soil or weather correct the situation. New products, no doubt, will become available.

Manganese

This element can be deficient, or it may occur in toxic amounts. A shortage of manganese is the most common micronutrient deficiency of soybeans. It is linked to pH, soil type, and organic matter. On silt loams and finer-textured soils, it seldom occurs below pH 6.5. On the other hand, it occurs on sandy soils that are high in organic matter and as low as pH 6.2, in the case of coastal sands in North Carolina. It sometimes occurs on muck and peat soils down to pH 5.8.

Manganese deficiency causes plants to be stunted. The leaves are yellow to whitish, but have green veins. Iron deficiency has the same symptoms. Manganese deficiency is most pronounced in cool weather and thus in the Midwest is most often seen in early to mid-June. It is correspondingly earlier in southern states. As the weather improves, soybeans often outgrow mild deficiencies.

Applications of phosphate fertilizers often correct mild manganese shortages. This is because the first reaction products of most phosphates (except diammonium phosphate) are strongly acid, thus lowering the pH and bringing manganese into solution around the fertilizer granules. Meeting the need of soybeans for manganese by adding phosphorus fertilizers is, of course, not the most profitable method unless phosphorus is also needed.

Manganese deficiency can be treated in three ways:
1. Spray a manganese sulfate (24 percent manganese) solution on the leaves, preferably when the plants are about 10 inches tall. Suggested rates vary among states from ½ to 2 pounds of actual manganese per acre (2 to 8 pounds of manganese sulfate) in 20 gallons of water. One spraying is usually enough. If a chelate is used, follow the label directions.
2. Mix manganese in an acid-forming fertilizer and band it near the row. The low pH in the band will keep the manganese in available form. The suggested rate is 6 pounds of manganese (25 pounds of manganese sulfate or 12½ pounds of manganous oxide—48 percent manganese) but this should be checked with a state extension agent or a well-informed dealer. Banding is often five times as effective as broadcasting, due to less contact with the soil and the lower pH in the band.
3. Apply chelated manganese if a suitable formulation is available. Fritted manganese compounds are mixed with fertilizer and either broadcast or banded.

Yearly applications of manganese are needed because the soil ties it up in unavailable form.

Soil testing for manganese is not very reliable, because the test level of the element changes rapidly, depending upon the soil moisture. Also, differences in drainage and organic matter within a field influence the test. Plant analysis is helpful in diagnosing a deficiency, provided no other nutrient is limiting.

Manganese toxicity is believed to be the most common cause of poor soybean growth on strongly acid soils (molybdenum deficiency is also an important factor on some soils). The characteristic symptom of cupped, crinkled leaves on stunted plants often occurs below pH 5.0. The toxicity is corrected by liming mineral soils to pH 6.0 or above and organic soils to at least pH 5.5.

Molybdenum

Molybdenum differs from the other micronutrients in that availability increases with rising pH. Most states report that molybdenum is seldom lacking for soybeans at pH 6.0 or above. However, Mississippi researchers suggest a molybdenum seed treatment even when pH is at the optimum level.

Legumes need molybdenum for nitrogen fixation. The deficiency symptom is pale green or yellow plants, typical of nitrogen shortage. The symptom is really caused by a lack of nitrogen, rather than a lack of molybdenum in the leaf tissue. The symptom usually does not occur on any soil that is high enough in nitrogen to make up for the lack of nodule fixation.

Agronomists in the southern United States report a lack of molybdenum under these conditions: strongly weathered and leached soils that developed from limestone but are now quite acid; coastal sands which are both naturally low in molybdenum and strongly leached; soils high in manganese and iron — and often strongly acid; small areas of soils that developed from serpentine.

Sodium molybdate (30 percent molybdenum) and ammonium molybdate (48 percent molybdenum) are used as seed treatments to supply ½ ounce per acre. Soil treatment is two to four ounces per acre.

After the pH of his acid soil has been raised to 6.0, a grower should get the latest information from his state experiment station and extension service about whether to add molybdenum. Several southern states recommend maintaining soil pH in the narrow range of 6.0 to 6.3 in order to maintain availability of both molybdenum and manganese. There is no soil test for molybdenum.

Zinc

Soybeans are much less sensitive to zinc deficiency than corn. This means that a grower can assume that his soybeans have an adequate supply of this element if his corn grows normally on the same soils.

Zinc-deficient soybean plants are stunted. The leaves are yellow or light green. The lower leaves may turn brown and drop. Flowers are scarce. The few pods that do set are abnormal and slow-maturing. In mild deficiencies, early growth is stunted and plants are very light green or chlorotic.

Zinc deficiency is most likely on soils with a high

19. Soil pH affects the availability of plant nutrients. The thicker the bar, the more of the nutrient is available. The best overall balance is between pH 6.0 and 7.0. Aluminum is not a plant nutrient, but is shown to indicate that it, along with manganese, is present in toxic amounts at very low pH.

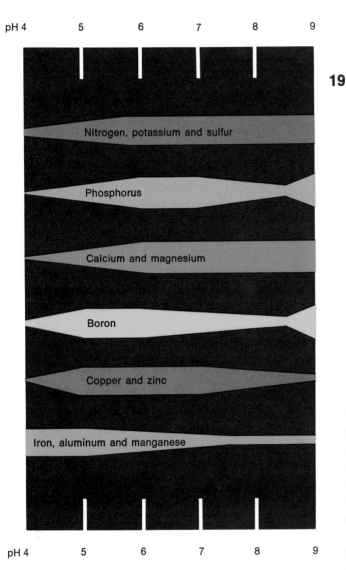

19

pH, high phosphorus, and low organic matter, especially subsoils exposed by land-forming operations. Soybeans on sandy soils are more susceptible than those on finer-textured soils. The deficiency can be caused by heavy phosphorus fertilization, especially near the row.

When the zinc supply is barely adequate, a phosphorus fertilizer program should be planned carefully with the advice of local extension agents or fertilizer dealers to avoid causing a deficiency. It appears that an increase in the phosphorus or zinc supply in the soil should be accompanied by a corresponding increase in the other nutrient to maintain yield on borderline soils. Nitrogen favors zinc uptake; iron suppresses it.

Zinc sulfate is the most widely applied inorganic zinc source. Zinc may also be formulated as a chloride, oxysulfate, ammonium sulfate, or ammonium phosphate. A single broadcast application normally is adequate for two to four years. Several organic chelates are also available. Florida agronomists suggest a foliar application of 2 pounds of zinc sulfate per 100 gallons of water. One zinc manufacturer recommends 1 to 2 pounds of 14.2 percent chelated zinc (about 2 to 4 ounces of zinc) per acre in enough water to wet the foliage thoroughly. For soil application, the company recommends 1½ to 5 pounds of product in the band at planting or later sidedressing.

Zinc toxicity has been known for many years near industrial plants that exhaust large amounts of the

The soil pH range

20	pH 9	Very strongly alkaline	pH this high is found only in arid or semi-arid regions. Soybeans seldom grown on such soils.
	pH 8	Strongly alkaline	Micronutrient deficiencies, especially manganese
		Slightly alkaline	and iron, are common in soybeans on some soils at this pH.
	pH 7	Neutral	Best range for soybeans and most other field crops although alfalfa and clover need pH of 6.5
		Slightly acid	or higher. Manganese may be deficient on
	pH 6	Moderately acid	soybeans on some soils above pH 6.3. (see text)
	pH 5	Strongly acid	Manganese and aluminum toxicity are common. Molybdenum is deficient in some soils. Decay
	pH 4	Very strongly acid	of residues is slow, N and P availability is low.

element into the air. Toxic levels can also be built up by repeated zinc applications, especially on acid soils.

Forms of Fertilizer

Fertilizer is commonly available in five forms — gas, liquid, slurry, suspension, and solids. Anhydrous ammonia, a popular source of nitrogen, is the only fertilizer considered to be a gas. Actually, it is a liquid kept under high pressure until the moment of application in the field.

The other four forms of fertilizer — liquid, slurry, suspension, and solid — can be used to supply all plant nutrients. These physical forms of plant food should be selected or eliminated on the basis of cost, convenience, and ease of handling and application. All are capable of giving good crop results. It is the chemical compound, rather than physical form, that determines how fertilizer reacts in the soil and how readily it is available to crops.

Questions are sometimes raised about liquid fertilizer being more quickly available than dry fertilizer. In a moist soil, the soluble part of dry fertilizer quickly absorbs water and goes into solution, mostly within a day. It is four to six days before the soybean roots enter the fertilizer band. For this reason, dry fertilizer has plenty of time to dissolve and meet the needs of the young seedling.

Since most dry fertilizers are somewhat hygroscopic (attracted to water), they will go into solution, even in moderately dry soils. Often, the fertilizer band can be found by looking for a dark, moist zone. In a very dry soil, a dry fertilizer obviously will not dissolve. On the other hand, liquid fertilizer usually will crystallize in an extremely dry soil. If soil is so dry that solid fertilizers cannot dissolve and liquids crystallize out of solution, seed will not germinate; neither will the roots of established plants take up nutrients.

To summarize, both liquid and soluble dry fertilizers will soon go into solution in moist soil and both will be found as dry pellets or crystals in an extremely dry soil.

Only about a pint of water is supplied with liquid fertilizer in 6 to 10 feet of row. That is not enough to increase germination in a dry soil, especially in view of the fact that it is purposely placed away from the seed. Even more important, the concentration of fertilizer salts in liquids (or around dry fertilizers) is high enough that plant roots cannot easily extract the water.

When the total amount of nutrients is equal, liquid and dry fertilizers are likely to cause the same amount of injury if placed too close to the seed. When properly placed, neither will impair germination. Liquid-mixed fertilizers are handicapped somewhat for soybeans, because nitrogen, used in formulating them, is not widely recommended for soybeans.

Water Solubility of Dry Fertilizer

Some dry-mixed fertilizer is made up of granules of

21. An indicator solution kit can be used to check soil pH in the field. The solution changes color as the pH varies. After the indicator has been in contact with the soil, its color is compared to a color chart calibrated for pH level.

22. Applying lime to correct low soil pH is one of the very first steps toward increasing soybean yields. Lime spreading equipment has made remarkable advances in recent years.

uniform composition. Each granule contains all of the nutrients guaranteed on the label. This type fertilizer is made chemically by combining the nutrients in solution and then precipitating them out by evaporating water from the mix. The dry pellets are completely water soluble.

There are at least two other types of dry-mixed fertilizer. One is the typical ammoniated super or triple-superphosphate pellet in which nutrients are combined partly by chemical action and partly by physical mixture of finely divided powder.

The second, commonly used in dry-mixed or bulk-blend fertilizer, can be made by two methods. If made with diammonium phosphate, the blend is a mixture of two types of pellets — one which contains nitrogen and phosphorus, and one containing potassium. If made without diammonium phosphate, the blend contains three different types of granules — one each for nitrogen, phosphorus, and potassium.

These latter two types — the ammoniated phosphate and bulk-blend fertilizer — are somewhat less water soluble than the granules of uniform composition. Under some conditions, water solubility is important, under others, it is of little consequence.

For band application on soils that test low in phosphorus, 50 percent solubility is adequate for soils below pH 7.0. On soils above pH 7.0, 80 percent water solubility is preferred. For broadcast applications on soils below pH 7.0, the degree of water solubility is unimportant. Where the pH is above 7.0 at least 50

percent water solubility is preferred even for broadcast applications.

The higher the soil test for phosphorus, the less important is water solubility because the crop gets more phosphorus from the soil and thus depends less on the fertilizer. The more phosphorus fertilizer the grower applies at one time, the less important is water solubility. For fertilizers with high water solubility, large pellets or granules are preferred. Small granules are better for fertilizers with lower water solubility.

Pesticides Mixed with Liquid Fertilizer

The need to save time and trips over fields causes many growers to consider mixing chemicals for a single application. Before mixing weed killers or insecticides with liquid fertilizer, a grower should get the answers to these three questions: First, are the emulsions, solutions, or suspensions compatible? This can be checked by mixing a small batch in a glass jar and observing whether separation occurs. If gentle stirring corrects the situation, the normal agitation in the sprayer may keep the emulsion in suitable condition. Second, will the ingredients react chemically so that either or both are ineffective? This information can be obtained from the technical personnel of either the fertilizer or pesticide supplier. Third, is the proposed time and placement suitable for both materials? Sideband placement on one side of the row is, for example, acceptable for fertilizer but not for a soil insecticide.

Lime for Soybeans

Liming medium to strongly acid soils is the very first step toward increasing soybean yields. This is true because:

— Manganese and aluminum toxicity can be prevented by liming acid soils.

— The growth of nodule-forming bacteria on soybean roots is favored by proper use of lime, thus allowing nitrogen fixation.

— Liming favors the growth of micro-organisms which decay plant residues and free plant nutrients.

— Liming increases the availability of some micronutrients.

— Liming releases phosphorus already in the soil and keeps newly applied phosphorus more available.

— Liming corrects calcium and magnesium deficiencies which may occur on strongly acid soils.

Soil acidity indicates the relative proportion of acids (hydrogen and aluminum) to bases (calcium, magnesium, potassium, sodium, ammonium). The proportion is measured on the pH scale, ranging from 0 to 14. When the two are in balance, the pH is 7.0.

Best pH for Soybeans

Soybeans grow best between pH 5.8 and 7.0. Most state extension services suggest that the pH be kept between 6.0 and 6.5, although 6.3 is the maximum in a few southern states because higher pH causes manganese deficiency. On soils inherently high in manganese and acidity, small yield increases were obtained by raising pH even above 6.5 in limited studies in southern Illinois and Missouri.

Fortunately soybeans, corn, and small grains have about the same pH need, allowing them to be grown in rotation, without a special liming program for each crop. In a cropping system including alfalfa or clover the pH goal should be at least 6.5. If this causes a manganese shortage in soybeans, the crop can be sprayed with manganese solution.

Tests for Lime Need

There are several ways to determine the amount of limestone needed for soybeans. Some tests measure only the *degree* of acidity; others measure *degree* and *amount*. The difference is best seen in the following example: The *degree* of acidity compares with the volume of water at a particular temperature. You may, for example, have either a cupful or a pailful of boiling water. The temperature of the water (degree) is the same in both containers, but the water in the pail has more total heat (amount) and more ice is required to cool it.

The amount of acidity depends upon the number of clay and humus units. This explains why a silty clay and sandy soil at the same pH have totally different liming requirements. The silty clay has far more clay units and thus a greater amount of acidity. After a pH test indicates the *degree* of acidity, the *amount* of acidity to be offset by limestone must be taken into account.

Indicator solutions, used for many years in laboratories, are still the most practical for testing in the field. They measure only the *degree* of acidity. In clay soils, the color of the indicator is often difficult to see immediately because the clay makes a muddy suspension. The best technique is to leave the indicator in contact with the soil with little or no stirring. The indicator will develop the proper color, indicating pH without becoming too cloudy.

The pH meter has been the most widely used laboratory test for many years. It measures only the *degree* of acidity.

The buffer method, used in about one-third of the states, takes into account both *degree* and *amount* of acidity so nobody has to estimate the percentages of clay and organic matter. This test gives a direct reading of lime requirement.

A soil test may show pH only, or both a water pH and salt pH. When fertilizer, a combination of salts, in most cases, is added to soil low in fertility, the pH reading sometimes declines a full unit. An increasing number of laboratories, therefore, determine pH both in distilled water and in a salt solution in order to get comparable readings on infertile and highly fertile soils. But since most state extension agronomists have already calibrated the response to lime with water pH, they prefer it to salt pH.

Liming Materials

Agricultural limestone is the most economical soil-neutralizing material, except for special situations. It is calcium carbonate ($CaCO_3$) with magnesium ranging from a trace to as much as 45 percent magnesium carbonate ($MgCO_3$). When it contains a significant amount of magnesium (perhaps a minimum of 5 to 10 percent), it is called *dolomitic* limestone.

Limestone value depends upon its acid-neutralizing power (total neutralizing power or calcium carbonate equivalent) and the speed at which it acts (influenced by fineness). Pure calcium carbonate has a neutralizing value of 100. Pure dolomite is about 108, because magnesium, pound for pound, neutralizes more acidity than calcium.

Hydrated lime is an accelerated-action, very fine powder with a neutralizing value of about 135. It is costly, and used mostly on high-value specialty crops where a very quick increase in pH is needed.

Marl is a natural carbonate deposit of marine animal shells that formed in shallow lakes. Since it has varying amounts of clay and organic matter as impurities, its neutralizing power is lower than limestone. It costs more than agricultural limestone in most areas.

Gypsum No Substitute for Lime

This useful source of calcium definitely does not neutralize soil acidity and therefore is not effective in improving yields on acid soils. Gypsum is used on alkali soils (high pH) in low rainfall areas. All of the excess sodium is replaced by the calcium. The sodium then leaches downward by rainfall or in irriga-

tion water. Excess sodium is not a problem on high pH (alkaline, rather than alkali) soils in humid regions. So-called "slick spots" in some midwestern states contain excess sodium but they are not high in pH. Gypsum treatment has been tried, but with little practical success.

Amount of Limestone

After a soybean grower receives his soil test results he should consider the quality of limestone to be used and the most profitable program for his cropping system.

In the long term, *neutralizing power* (sometimes called calcium carbonate equivalent) is the most important factor because it denotes the power of the liming material to neutralize acidity. Neutralizing power In commercial limestones ranges from about 80 to 108 percent of that of pure calcium carbonate.

In the short term, *fineness* of grind is important because it governs how quickly the limestone works. Limestone finer than 60 mesh will be available in the first year; that finer than 30 mesh, in two or three years. Material coarser than ⅛ inch is only one-fourth available in eight years. From this it can be seen that a grower can afford to pay more for extra-fine limestone if he needs a quick effect. On the other hand, it is obvious that moderate fineness is acceptable for maintenance applications after the pH goal has been reached.

There are differences in the dollar-for-dollar value of limestones from various sources. It usually pays to shop around for the right combination of neutralizing power and fineness.

Regional Differences In Liming

There are some important differences in liming southern and midwestern soils:
— Coastal plain soils along the Atlantic seaboard and gulf coast are moderately to strongly acid. Nearly all Mississippi bottomland soils from the Missouri Bootheel through Tennessee, Arkansas, Mississippi, and Louisiana require lime. Midwestern soils range from strongly acid to alkaline, but in general are higher in pH than southern soils.
— The soil pH for soybeans must be controlled within a narrower range on coastal plain soils than elsewhere. A pH of 5.7 to 6.3 is practical, but 6.0 to 6.2 is ideal. Below 6.0, molybdenum becomes progressively more deficient; above 6.3 manganese may be deficient.
— Delta and midwestern soils will usually tolerate at least pH 6.5 without a manganese shortage; molybdenum shortage is seldom a problem.
— Coastal plain and piedmont soils usually require much less limestone than delta or midwestern soils of identical texture and acidity to raise the pH to a given level. This is due to differences in types of clay. Southern clays have a much lower exchange capacity. The delta soils, which formed from midwestern sediments, are much like Corn Belt soils.

Sampling map for a 40- to 60-acre field

24. In fields that have been cropped and fertilized uniformly in recent years, soil samples should be taken in a regular pattern. Each numbered sample consists of five separate, small samples mixed together. A record should be kept of the location of each sample so different limestone and fertilizer treatments can be applied if called for by soil test results. In fields lacking uniformity, each area should be represented by one or more samples, each consisting of subsamples.

— Coastal plain soils in southern states and along the Atlantic seaboard are low in magnesium, so dolomitic limestone is usually suggested. Other southern and midwestern soils rarely have a magnesium shortage if the pH is 6.0 or higher.

Small Amounts of Fine Limestone in the Row

A few farmers each year ask whether 200 to 300 pounds of extra-fine limestone placed near the soybean row will substitute temporarily for a regular lime application. They often refer to rented or newly bought fields. Little research has been reported on localized light liming. A few limestone suppliers report that they have some customers who are satisfied with the practice. An Illinois test on strongly acid soil (pH 4.2) showed little response to 300 pounds of lime drilled to the side and below soybean seed.

If light liming has a place, it is most likely to be where phosphorus and potassium are adequate. It may be of value where the pH is only slightly below the desired levels, perhaps 5.2 to 5.5, and as a stop-gap measure on fields held under a short-term lease.

Any farmer who tries light liming should leave several rows untreated for a check. However, it probably will be impossible to see a difference unless it is at least 20 percent.

Crop Removal and Leaching Loss

Limestone leaches very little on acid soils (except sands). This is because the calcium and magnesium carbonates replace hydrogen on the particles of clay and organic matter particles, and are held against leaching.

Proper use of limestone continues to be important because nitrogen fertilizers acidify the soil. Most forms of nitrogen cause enough acidity to replace about two pounds of pure calcium carbonate for each pound of nitrogen. For ammonium sulfate the figure is 5.4 pounds.

Taking Good Soil Samples

Poorly taken samples may cause a grower to apply unneeded lime and fertilizer, or to omit applications where a highly profitable increase could be obtained. Here are some guidelines for sampling soils:
— Never scrimp on the number of samples. In fields that have been limed and fertilized several times, tests vary as much as 50 percent, even though the soil type does not vary and the field looks uniform.
— Keep separate samples from parts of a field that have been cropped, fertilized, limed, or manured differently. Also sample different soil type areas separately.
— Avoid sampling directly in the crop row and in the fertilizer band. The test will be too low in the row and too high in the band.
— Take samples from the plow layer only, whether it is 6 or 12 inches. Samples taken from greater depths include soil below the fertilized zone, causing test results to be too low. An exception to this

Reliability of soil tests

The reliability of soil tests for predicting various nutrient responses. For several of the micronutrients, and perhaps some secondary nutrients, spectrographic analyses of plant tissues when calibrations have been further developed will be more useful than soil tests to indicate future treatments.

Lime requirement — good
Phosphorus — good
Potassium — good
Boron — fair
Calcium — fair
Zinc — fair
Magnesium — poor
Copper (organic soils) — poor
Nitrogen — poor
Iron — poor
Manganese — fair to poor
Molybdenum — none
Sulfur — poor

is the suggested sampling of the subsoil just once, for possible use later in making soil fertility comparisons.
— Make a field map showing sampling locations. This may reveal patterns of high and low fertility requiring special treatment.
— Keep records of fertilizer, manure, and lime applications through the years.
— Resample every four to six years.
— When sending in soil samples, include complete information on soil type, cropping history, and previous soil treatments. This is needed by the person who interprets the tests.

The critical soil tests for most soybean growers are for pH, phosphorus, and potassium. The laboratory procedures are well-established and many field trials have been conducted to show the relationship between various test levels and crop response to treatment.

Soil tests are of little value until they are calibrated (the response to treatment determined for different test levels) for the grower's general soil situation. Laboratories are asked by an increasing number of farmers to make micronutrient tests for which they cannot give an interpretation. Good farmers are understandably eager to learn all they can about possible needs for micronutrients, but tests that cannot be interpreted are costly to the farmer and serve no purpose. Plant analyses are more helpful than soil tests for determining the level of most micronutrients.

Interpreting Soil Tests

Ideally, after a soil is tested, an experienced agronomist should discuss the entire crop and fertility plan with the grower. Most county extension agents are trained to do this, and many fertilizer dealers offer this service. But such personalized service is not always possible. Computers are used to fill this gap in reporting and interpreting soil test results.

Once an agronomist has developed the proper set of directions for the computer, the interpretations are made automatically, releasing the agronomist to do other work. Also, because the machine works so rapidly, more factors can be considered than in the case of manual interpretations. These factors include soil texture, drainage, organic matter, previous treatments, cropping system, and fertilizer placement. But computer results are no better than input data. A computer gives equal weight to research-based facts and opinions based on mere observation or heresay.

Handling Variable Tests from a Field

Tests within a single field often range from low to high. If there are only a few very high tests, it is best to ignore them. If high tests occur consistently in large parts of the field, and low tests in other large parts, each can be treated separately. But if high, medium, and low tests are mixed at random, the average of the lower half of the tests is suggested as a guide to fertilizing and liming. Growers who do a superior job in all other areas of crop management are usually en-

26. These tentative standards for interpreting soybean plant analyses were developed at the Ohio Agricultural Research and Development Center. The optimum level for some nutrients is affected by the amounts of certain other nutrients.

Standard nutrient levels in soybean plants

	Element	Deficient	Low	Sufficient	High	Excess
		Less than				More than
Percent	N	4.00	4.00-4.50	4.51-4.50	5.51-7.00	7.00
	P	0.15	0.16-0.25	0.26-0.50	0.50-0.80	0.80
	K	1.25	1.26-1.70	1.71-2.50	2.51-2.75	2.75
	Ca	0.20	0.21-0.35	0.36-2.00	2.01-3.00	3.00
	Mg	0.10	0.11-0.25	0.26-1.00	1.01-1.50	1.51
Parts per million	Mn	14	15- 20	21-100	101-250	250
	Fe	30	31- 50	51-350	350-500	500
	B	10	11- 20	21- 55	56- 80	80
	Cu	4	5- 9	10- 30	31- 50	50
	Zn	10	11- 20	21- 50	50- 75	75
	Mo	0.4	0.5-0.9	1.0- 5.0	5.1-10.0	10.0

26

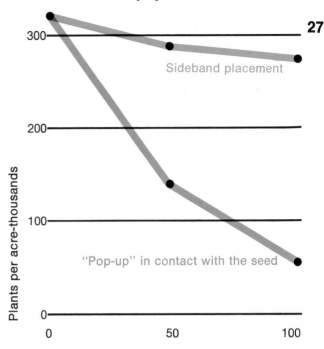

Pounds of 7-28-14 fertilizer in the row

27. Soybeans are very sensitive to fertilizer injury. Stands were heavily reduced when fertilizer was placed in contact with the seed, but placment of the same rates of fertilizer just 1½ inches beside and below the seed allowed good stand survival in studies at Dixon Springs, Illinois.

couraged to apply more fertilizer than those who do only an average job.

Improper Soil Test Use

Some people mistakenly believe that a soil test measures the pounds of nutrients that will be available to the crop throughout the growing season. Based on this misunderstanding, they set up a fertilizer accounting system as follows: a 60-bushel crop of soybeans contains 65 pounds of P_2O_5 in the seed, pods, stems, and leaves. Assume that the soil test shows 31 pounds, and that plant residues from the previous crop may supply 10 pounds, making a total of 41. The deficiency appears to be 24 pounds of P_2O_5. Reasoning further, they assume that soybeans can utilize no more than 15 percent of the fertilizer phosphorus in the year of application. They therefore say that they should apply about 158 pounds of P_2O_5. Soil test results should not be used in this manner.

Soil tests for phosphorus, for example, cannot simply be plugged into such an equation because of at least three factors. First, the extracting solution does not dissolve all of the chemical compounds containing available phosphorus. The amount dissolved depends not only on the strength of the extracting solution, but also on how much is used per gram of soil and the extraction time. Second, all laboratories do not use the same chemical extracting procedures. Third, the test extracts phosphorus for

only a few minutes on a sample taken from the plow layer, while the soybean plant feeds for several months to a depth of three to six feet.

The results of a soil test have practical meaning only when research has been conducted to show the crop response to fertilizer applied at different test levels. Some states have a single set of suggested rates for all soils, others have widely different rates for various soil types.

Plant Analyses

Three general classes of tests are made on growing plants:

— Tissue tests measure only the soluble contents of the plant sap. These are, in essence, enroute from the point of entry to the point where they will be used in the plant.

— Chemical analyses measure the soluble materials in the cell sap plus the elements that have already been incorporated into plant tissues.

— Spectrographic analyses are done on an instrument capable of testing for all essential elements at once, except nitrogen and sulfur. The elements are excited by heat and high voltage and each then gives off light of a characteristic wave length.

28

28. High-capacity fertilizer applicators equipped with flotation tires represent a breakthrough in making broadcast applications. The large flotation tires minimize compaction and formation of ruts when used on wet or plowed soil. The big units carry 1,000 gallons of liquid fertilizer at field speeds of 10 to 12 miles per hour, and up to 6 tons of dry fertilizer at speeds of up to 20 miles per hour.

The results of all forms of plant analyses are usually available too late for treatments to be made during the crop year. The main use of the results is in planning corrective applications for the next year.

Tissue Tests

Tissue tests have been used since the mid-1940's to help diagnose crop troubles. They can be made right on the spot. They help to identify hidden hunger where a deficiency is not serious enough to cause recognizable symptoms, or to confirm a diagnosis of deficiency based on visible signs.

Tissue tests should be made about every 14 days from the time soybeans are 12 inches tall until they reach full height and begin to develop pods. A single test does not tell whether the nutrient level is going up or down; the trend is often more significant than an absolute level. If only one test is to be made, the best time is just before or during early flowering. There is not complete agreement on the plant part to test. Some suggest testing the petiole; others, the swollen base of the petiole. Best advice is to follow the instructions that accompany the tissue test kit.

Some sources of test kits and refill materials are:

Denham Laboratory
Route 1
Wilmer, Alabama 36587

Urbana Laboratories
Urbana, Illinois 61801

Lee Lab
1412 Russell Blvd.
Columbia, Missouri 65201

A tissue test may reveal that a nutrient is present in an inadequate amount, but it may fail to pinpoint the cause of the problem. A low test may be due to several things. First, it is possible that the nutrient is available in small amounts in the soil. A soil test and fertilization history of the field usually can verify this. Second, the soil may be too wet or too dry to get a good test of the plant tissue. Third, trouble with the root system could be limiting nutrient uptake as a result of soil compaction, insect damage, or root pruning during cultivation.

A high test, on the other hand, can be misleading. It could result from having a small, but concentrated, amount of phosphorus fertilizer in the row that will be exhausted long before the growth period has ended. It also could be due to a shortage of some other nutrient which, if added, would result in extra growth and perhaps then a shortage or phosphorus.

Chemical Analyses

Chemical analyses are not generally available to farmers. They are used mainly by research workers because of high cost and the fact that they must be made in a laboratory.

Spectrographic Analyses

The spectrograph provides a test for several micronutrients for which there is no satisfactory soil test. It also can test for many major, secondary, and micronutrients at the same time and do it faster than chemical analyses. The factor that limits the number of tests is the time required to weigh, grind, and ash samples rather than the time the sample is in the spectrograph. When spectrographic analysis is used, the grower who sends a soybean plant from a problem part of the field should send in one from a normal area, too. A normal plant from the same field is the best reference for comparison of plant composition.

Row Placement of Fertilizer

Row fertilization has been the rule in the South and along the Atlantic Coast, but not in the Midwest. Suggestions for this method of fertilizing soybeans are as follows:

— There is a definite trend away from row fertilizer where phosphorus and potassium tests are medium to high.

— Most extension agronomists indicate that needed phosphorus and potassium can be applied either near the row or broadcast. At low pH, band application of phosphorus is slightly favored. The suggested amount of phosphorus is about twice as high for broadcast as for row placement, but the carryover effect usually equalizes the cost in a few years.

— Fertilizer should not be placed in direct contact with the seed (pop-up), because it may damage the stand. Suggested distance away from the seed ranges from 1½ inches to the side and 1½ inches below seed on fine-textured silt and clay soils to 3 to 5 inches to the side and 2 to 4 inches below on sandy soils.

Broadcast Fertilization

The trend is definitely toward broadcast application of phosphorus and potassium for all field crops, especially soybeans. Broadcasting eliminates the danger of fertilizer injury and is faster and requires less labor. It can be done in the off-season, thus interfering less with planting. Broadcast plant nutrients cost less, due to bulk handling. And nutrients are more available in dry periods when fertilizer is broadcast and plowed down.

However, there are some disadvantages of broadcasting. It results in more soil-fertilizer contact, possibly reducing the availability of phosphorus and several micronutrients in either strongly acid or strongly alkaline soils. Heavy spreading equipment running on wet fields may cause ruts or compaction, although this can be minimized with flotation tires. About twice as much phosphorus must be applied for equal effect the first year. This is offset, however, by the carryover in the following years. And finally, at very low phosphorus and potassium test levels, results from broadcasting alone often fail to equal either row application or a combination of row and broadcast applications.

Relative salt concentration

Fertilizer	Relative salt index per pound of $N + P_2O_5 + K_2O$
Nitrate of Soda, 16.5% N	100.0
Sulphate of Potash-Magnesia, 21.9% K_2O	32.5
Muriate of Potash, 60% K_2O	31.9
Nitrate of Potash, 13.8% N, 46.6% K_2O	20.1
Sulphate of Potash, 54% K_2O	14.1
Diammonium Phosphate, 21.2% N, 53.8% P_2O_5	7.5
Monoammonium Phosphate 12.2% N, 61.7% P_2O_5	6.7
Superphosphate, 20% P_2O_5	6.4
Superphosphate, 48% P_2O_5	3.5

29. Salt index or concentration indicates the likelihood of "fertilizer burn" when fertilizer is in contact with germinating seed or young roots. These values are for chemically pure fertilizer materials compared to nitrate of soda. (Adapted from L. F. Radar, Jr., L. M. White, and C. W. Whittaker, "Soil Science," 1943.)

No-Plow Systems

In the various no-plow systems for soybeans, phosphorus and potassium are left mainly on or near the soil surface. Where the fertility level is already high throughout the plow layer, a grower need not worry about a yield loss from shallow placement for several years. If, on the other hand, fertility is so low that a good response could be expected from properly placed fertilizer and a dry season occurs, shallow-placed fertilizer will be less effective.

The disadvantage from shallow-placed fertilizer in a residue system is less, however, than in a clean-tilled system. The mulch helps to keep the surface soil moist and thus more favorable for root growth and nutrient uptake.

Foliar Feeding

Certain nutrients can be supplied more efficiently to some crops through liquid sprays than through soil applications. This technique bypasses the capacity of strongly acid or alkaline soil to fix certain nutrients in chemical forms unavailable to the plant. Leaf feeding is not an economical method of supplying nitrogen, phosphorus, and potassium to field crops. It is acceptable for some micronutrients. Foliar application has not been studied extensively in field crops, but three questions can be raised about its efficiency:

— When soybean plants are 8 to 10 inches tall, will most of the spray miss the leaves and fall onto the soil surface?

— Will rainfall wash off much of the phosphorus and potassium?

— Since these nutrients move very little and roots cannot feed in dry surface soil, isn't the soil surface the poorest place to have phosphorus and potassium in midsummer?

Fertilizer "Burn"

Soybeans are especially sensitive to injury from concentration of nitrogen and potassium salts around the germinating seed or seedling roots. When the salt concentration outside the roots is greater than that inside the roots, water moves from the roots and the seedling wilts. In extreme cases it dies. If only part of the root system is affected, the plant survives but is stunted. From this description of the cause of injury, it follows that injury is worst when too much fertilizer with a high salt index is placed close to the seed, when dry weather occurs soon after planting, causing

30

the salt solution to be more concentrated, and on sandy soils, which hold less water per unit volume of soil, thus resulting in a higher salt concentration.

Injury to soybeans can be avoided by broadcasting all the fertilizer or keeping row application, especially of nitrogen and potassium, to safe levels for the soil type and at a safe distance from the seed. (On sandy soils row fertilizer should be limited to about 30 pounds of nitrogen and potassium when placed 1½ inches to the side and 1½ inches below the seed. If placed three or more inches away, the amount can be increased by about one-half. On silt loams and other fine-textured soils, the safe limits are about 50 percent greater than on sands.)

Beware the Fertility "Quack"

Fly-by-night peddlers of unproven fertilizers claim spectacular benefits, often stating that their material is a natural product with mystical qualities. They do not guarantee content of the major nutrients, and thereby avoid state fertilizer laws. They often claim micronutrients in their product, but seldom guarantee the amounts or the availability of the nutrients. Their claims are not backed by research results from an unbiased source; instead, they give only farmer testimonials. Very often a letter of inquiry addressed to their home office will be returned unclaimed. They also make derogatory comments about the state experiment stations, county extension workers, and sometimes the local fertilizer dealers. However, the

legitimate fertilizer dealer, who occasionally offers a new product deserving an on-farm test, is not to be confused with the fertility quack.

Lodging and Fertility

Dr. R. L. Cooper, of the USDA, has shown that the potential response of soybeans to very high fertility levels may be lost if the plants lodge. When soybeans lodge, the leaf area is not oriented for efficient use of energy from the sun. Many of the lower and center leaves are completely shaded and die prematurely, to the detriment of yield.

How the Champions Fertilize Soybeans

The fertilizer practices of seven contest-winning growers offer some interesting comparisons. However, every grower should keep in mind that he does not know the soil type, soil test levels of phosphorus and potassium, nor soil pH on these farms. In some cases, winning yields are unprofitable because of unrealistic production costs.

Amount of fertilizer used ranges from none by Dean Chandler of Illinois (95.16 bushels per acre in 1967) and a low rate of 100 pounds of 5-20-20 by Ray Beason of Iowa (92.98 bushels in 1966) to rates of 1,400 pounds of nitrogen, 576 pounds of phosphorus, and 1,328 pounds of potassium by Harry Pick of Illinois (100.7 in 1968).

Accumulated versus freshly applied fertilizer can be compared in the winners' records. High yields pro-

30. In studying the relation of extra-high fertilization to lodging, researchers fertilize two rows identically, then support one row with string or wire and leave the other to the forces of nature. Research shows that much of the potential response to high fertility is lost in lodging.

duced by John Reiser of Illinois were made on fields that had been built to high fertility over a period of several years. In contrast, Harry Pick's winning yield in 1966 was on a field that had been only medium in pH (5.7), low in phosphorus, and medium to high in potassium. It was heavily fertilized for the 1966 crop.

Most winners applied both row and broadcast fertilizer. No single fertilizer practice was used by all winners.

Many farmers ask why contest-winning yields are 10 to 20 bushels per acre greater than yields in research plots. A partial answer is that the winners use all of the best practices known to researchers but the farmers have the advantage of thousands of locations. A widespread group of farmers has better odds of getting ideal rainfall, temperature, and less lodging than a few research fields. There is also greater precision in determining yields on the research plots.

Ultra-High Fertilization

Scientists have explored the possibility of using ultra-high fertilization rates to increase soybean yields. In one case, $60 worth of fertilizer produced an additional yield of only 1.9 bushels per acre. In other tests, high rates sometimes reduced yield. The results of many such tests show conclusively that simply adding more nitrogen, phosphorus and potassium where fertility is already high will not produce a breakthrough in soybean yields. Many growers, of course, can profit from using more lime and fertilizer where fertility has

not been built up to suggested levels.

Fertility Research for the Future

Some lines of research now in progress may lead to new ideas on fertilizing soybeans. In some tests, sources of carbon, such as coal or propane, are placed in the soil to reduce the amount of available nitrates early in the season and thus perhaps stimulate the production of more nodules. Foliar sprays are being tested to supply nutrients at times of greatest needs. And many trials are being conducted with secondary elements and micronutrients in areas where deficiences have not been identified.

5

Water Management

Water and carbon dioxide are the basic raw materials in the photosynthetic process. The demand for water is especially great, because it is more than just a raw material. It is the solvent in which gases and salts enter and move through the plant. It is the "hydraulic fluid" used to move plant parts and open and close the stomata (minute openings in the leaves). When open, the stomata release water vapor and other gases from the plant to the atmosphere. They also serve as entry points for carbon dioxide and other gases taken in by the plant.

Water, a constituent of cell protoplasm, is necessary for growth. It gives plants form. Take out the water and a plant becomes limp, with no body or form. Actively growing tissue is normally 85 to 95 percent water.

In most places where soybeans are grown, the amount of water used by the growing crop plus that lost by evaporation from the soil surface exceeds the normal rainfall during the growing season. This deficit, for example, is normally four to five inches at Urbana, Illinois. It must be recovered from water stored in the soil or from irrigation. On most farms where soybeans are grown, water from the soil profile fulfills the requirement.

The available water in a soil is measured by saturating it, letting it drain, and then growing a crop without supplemental water until the plants wilt and die. At this point there is still water in the soil but it is held so tightly that the plant cannot get enough to prevent wilting and death. The amount remaining in the soil when plants wilt varies by soil type. It ranges from about 5 percent in sand to 20 percent in clay.

The following shows how much water in various soils is actually available to plants:

Water availability

| Soil | Inches water per foot | | |
	Total content	Actually available	Percent available
Sandy	Less than 1.8	Less than 1.2	Less than 66%
Loamy	1.8 to 3.0	1.2 to 2.4	66 to 80%
Silty	3.0 to 4.2	2.4 to 3.6	80 to 86%
Clay	4.2 to 6.0	1.8 to 3.0	43 to 50%

University of Illinois.

In humid regions, the water available for soybeans per foot usually is higher on silt loams than on clays or clay loams. Furthermore, roots penetrate deeper into the subsoil on silt loam soil, which has better structure, is less compact, and is better aerated. What effect does chiseling or adding organic matter have on the availability of water in the soil?

— Unless there is a definite barrier to the downward growth of roots, such as a hardpan, chiseling has little effect on root penetration and the area from which water is drawn.

— The subsoil of many poorly drained clay soils below the reach of the chisel is often poor in structure, so the gain from subsoiling is limited.

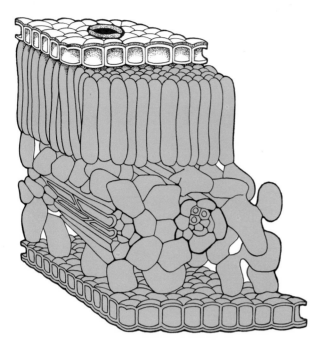

1. The surface of a soybean leaf is covered with tiny openings or stomata. These pores release water vapor and gases from the plant, and take in carbon dioxide and other gases. In darkness, the guard cells surrounding a stoma are limp and the stoma is closed; in the presence of light, the guard cells absorb water and become turgid, opening the stoma.

— The major contribution of organic matter to the soil water supply is that it increases the amount of rainfall that soaks in.
— Organic matter improves the aggregation of clays and silt loams, slightly increasing the water-holding capacity of soil.

A good step in making the most of rainfall is keeping the infiltration rate high. Obviously, water must enter the soil before it is available to the soybean plant. Infiltration may be increased and runoff reduced by leaving the crop residue on the surface. The presence of the residue prevents the running together of the soil and helps protect the aggregation of the surface soil. Good aggregation is essential for rapid infiltration. Secondary tillage normally destroys aggregation. Occasionally it may provide a temporary improvement when used to break up a hard crust. Generally, though, tillage operations should be held to an absolute minimum. This is especially true in the South where temperatures and evaporation losses may already be high at planting time. Excessive tillage prior to planting may contribute to the loss of moisture in the surface of the soil, with poor emergence as the result.

Farming on the contour will help reduce runoff on

Crop	Pounds water per pound of dry matter produced
Alfalfa	844
Soybeans	646
Oats	583
Potatoes	575
Wheat	545
Sugar beets	377
Corn	349
Sorghum	305

2. The soybean plant requires relatively large amounts of water when compared to some other crops. The amounts listed are only approximations. The water actually required by any crop depends on its environment.

sloping land. The benefits of this practice are especially great during the growing season but also extend into the rest of the year.

Efficient Use of Water

Once water enters the soil and is stored there, the main concern shifts to its efficient use. Water is lost by two means during the growing season: it evaporates from the soil into the atmosphere, and it is given off by plants during transpiration.

The energy of the sun is the primary force that causes evaporation and transpiration. The relative humidity and rate of air movement are also involved, but to a lesser degree than sunlight. In general, any practice that increases yield also increases water use efficiency. Therefore, the value of an adequately fertilized crop free of diseases, insects, and weeds is obvious.

The grower who studies and knows weather patterns may be able to make the most efficient use of field moisture. This is true because some areas consistently have a two or three week period without appreciable rainfall. Weather records indicate when such periods can be expected. Crop timing can be adjusted to avoid low-rainfall stress during the moisture-critical stages of germination, seedling establishment, and early pod filling. In adjusting crop timing it should be remembered that planting date is easily manipulated. The flowering time of midseason and early varieties is influenced more by planting date

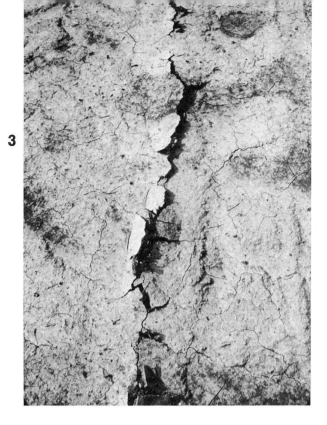

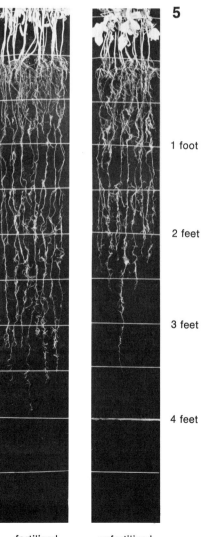

5

3. A hard soil crust is more than a barrier to the emerging soybean seedling; it also reduces the water-absorbing capacity of the field. Occasionally, the use of tillage may be justified to break crusts and reduce runoff.

4. Contour planting is an effective way of reducing runoff and making good use of rainfall on sloping fields.

5. Properly fertilized soybeans have more extensive roots than those suffering from plant food deficiencies, and are therefore able to make better use of soil moisture.

than that of full-season, adapted varieties. Therefore, it is both possible and necessary to match the flowering and pod set of the early and midseason varieties with periods of favorable rainfall.

In some sections, the optimum planting time may occur during a period of dry weather. If proper concern is given to conservation of moisture in the seedbed, it may be possible to ignore the low rainfall pattern and plant soybeans on schedule anyway. New developments in herbicides and equipment for planting and tillage will, no doubt, open new opportunities for making the most of the moisture during the growing season.

Narrow rows contribute to efficient water use under certain conditions. As long as the soil surface is moist, the total amount of water lost through evaporation and transpiration is nearly equal whether plants are large or small or rows wide or narrow. This is the case because narrow rows, high populations, and large leaf area shade the soil, thus reducing soil

1 foot

2 feet

3 feet

4 feet

fertilized   unfertilized

6. Plastic and chemical soil coverings have been used in researching the effect of restricting evaporation.

evaporation but increasing the loss from leaves. However, as long as the soil surface is moist, it is better to have water moved through the plant, thus contributing to crop yield, than to have water lost through soil surface evaporation.

Conditions change when the soil surface becomes dry. The rate of loss is reduced and part of the energy from the sun merely heats up the soil or air. Under this situation narrow rows increase the water stress because there is less shading of one plant by its neighbors and more sunlight strikes the leaves. The advantage of a good leaf canopy returns, of course, after each rain or irrigation.

Evaporation

Many soils hold enough moisture to produce 20 to 30 bushels of soybeans. In an experiment at Urbana, Illinois, for example, soybeans produced this much on stored moisture alone. A plastic mulch prevented rainfall from entering the soil. It also prevented evaporation during the growing season. This research showed that drouth may be eliminated if a practical method can be found to reduce moisture loss by evaporation.

The use of both plastic mulch and chemicals to reduce evaporation is being researched. In fact, plastic is used in the production of some high value crops now. However, the primary purposes of the covering are to provide weed control and to raise soil temperature. Hexadecanol and related chemicals have been

used for several years to suppress evaporation from ponds and reservoirs by making a film one molecule thick. These chemicals also reduce water loss when applied to soil, but the cost is prohibitive. Research is underway to explore the possibility of using chemicals of this type on plants. Scientists are also treating soils with chemicals that reduce the surface tension of water. This enables the water to enter the soil more rapidly, thus storing larger reserves.

Irrigation

Most soybeans grown in the United States are not irrigated. However, in the Midsouth and South, where facilities are available for irrigating cotton or rice, soybean irrigation is used. Some irrigation of soybeans is done in Nebraska, also.

The response of soybeans to irrigation is seldom as great as that of cotton or corn. Increases obtained by the University of Arkansas during a five-year irrigation experiment ranged from essentially zero to 23 bushels per acre (109 percent) for one variety and from zero to 19 bushels (92 percent) for another variety. Response to irrigation was negligible in two of the five years of the experiment.

The University of Missouri obtained yield increases of up to 30 bushels per acre on a Dexter sandy loam soil. But there was essentially no response to irrigation in one of the three years of the experiment.

The significant question is not whether irrigation will increase soybean yields, but instead, whether it

7

104

7. Furrow irrigation is one method of providing supplemental water to soybeans. Varieties planted in irrigated fields should be resistant to Phytophthora rot.

8. Sprinkler irrigation is used by soybean growers in some regions. High value crops may be grown ahead of soybeans to help bear the overhead costs of irrigation equipment.

will increase profits. If a grower has already made the capital investment in irrigation facilities for other crops, he may have better chances of making soybean irrigation pay than the farmer who does not spread his investment over several crops. Irrigation is not something to be tried in a small way like a new variety or herbicide. It requires a major investment from the outset.

The Cost of Installation and Operation

In humid regions, irrigation systems must be tailor-made for the individual farm. Therefore, an estimate by a person qualified to plan and install irrigation systems is the best source of information. The Agricultural Extension Service and the Soil Conservation Service offer such a service in some areas, as do private consultants and various distributors of irrigation equipment.

In general, a sprinkler system and deep well for 50 to 200 acres will cost $100 to $200 per irrigated acre. If water is taken from a stream, lake, or shallow well, the cost may decline to $75 to $100 per acre irrigated.

Operating costs average about $2 per acre-inch (27,000 gallons) of water from a deep well and somewhat less for a shallow well (15 feet or less), stream, or lake. At this rate, one six-inch application of water costs about $12 per acre. With almost any type of system, it takes at least one man-hour per acre per irrigation.

Soybean irrigation is most profitable on soils that cannot store large amounts of available water, such as sand, where high-value crops are grown to help pay the overhead costs, and where the cost of developing a water supply is relatively low.

The Water Supply

The potential user of irrigation should know the water rights in his state. In some states there are legal restrictions on the amount of water that can be taken from a stream or lake. The county extension service or Soil Conservation Service usually has information on local water rights.

Irrigation requires large amounts of water and the supply must be reliable. The greatest need will be during a drouth when small streams and farm ponds may be dry. To apply 2 inches of water to 100 acres requires 5,400,000 gallons (27,000 gallons per acre-inch x 2 x 100 acres = 5,400,000). The average farm pond holds 3 acre-feet of water or 972,000 gallons, when full. Theoretically, this is enough water to put 2 inches of water on 18 acres once, or 2 inches of water on 9 acres each week for 2 weeks. In reality, there would not be this much water in the pond because of the loss through evaporation.

Wells supply water for about one-third of the nation's irrigation systems. In most cases, deep wells are needed, but in some sandy and gravelly flood plains special pipes can be sunk to a water supply only 15 to 25 feet down. Both the supply and the quality of water should be checked. A test well (at a cost

Normal rainfall; April - September

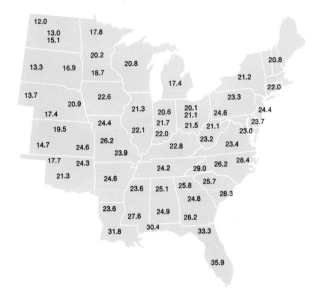

Average relative humidity, local noon, July

Percent

40-50	
50-60	
60-70	
over 70	

of $1.50 to $3.00 per foot) may be needed to determine whether the supply is adequate and whether the water is of good quality. Excessive salts or carbonates in the water are undesirable. The use of salty water may lead to poor tilth and low yields.

Frequency of Drouth

The chance of drouth is an important factor in deciding whether an irrigation system will pay. Long-time weather records for an area provide information on the frequency and severity of drouths during the growing season. Normal rainfall from April 1 to September 30 and relative humidity, which strongly influences the effectiveness of the rainfall, are shown above.

Type of Soil

Any soil that will absorb at least ¼-inch of water per hour can be irrigated. If the absorption rate is lower than ¼-inch, the sun on a hot day will cause excessive evaporation losses. The rate at which water is applied must be adjusted according to the absorption rate. Irrigation costs are greater the slower the absorption rate.

The frequency of irrigation depends on several factors, including the water-holding capacity of the soil. Within the rooting depth of soybeans, soils vary in available water storage capacity from about 5 inches in sands to at least 14 inches in silt loams. This explains the use of large numbers of irrigation systems

10. The normal rainfall for a region from April through September should be considered in making the decision to install irrigation equipment. Local weather records can give more specific information on rainfall amounts.

11. The average relative humidity at noon in July varies from under 40 to more than 70 percent in the soybean-producing states of the country. As relative humidity declines, evaporation and transpiration increase.

on sandy soils and their absence on nearby silt loams in some areas. It also explains the need to irrigate at short intervals on sandy soils and why less water per irrigation is normally applied to sands. In many states the Soil Conservation Service can supply irrigation guides giving estimated water-holding capacities for major soils.

Irrigation Increases Costs

The cost of growing soybeans is increased when an investment is made in irrigation equipment. This means good seed, effective weed control, and other efficient practices that contribute to maximizing yields are especially important.

When to Irrigate

There is little need to irrigate soybeans before they start to bloom and set pods if the soil moisture is completely recharged to a depth of six to eight feet before planting. If the soil is not carrying a full amount of moisture before planting, a preplant irrigation may be required.

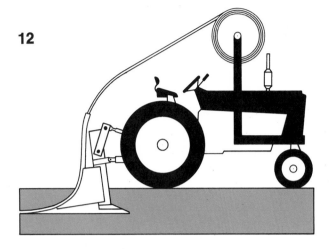

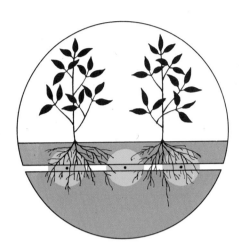

12. Subsurface irrigation of soybeans is being tested in some areas. Perforated plastic pipe is installed in the field below plowing depth (left). Later, the growing crop derives almost immediate benefit as the water is released in the root zone.

The exact soil moisture at which soybean irrigation should begin is not well-established. It is generally believed that after the soybeans have reached the flowering period, irrigation should begin when the available soil moisture drops much below 50 percent.

Three ways to decide when to irrigate are:

1. Buy and install commercial moisture meters in the field.

2. Judge by the soil "balling" method. About 50 percent of the available water has been used at the 8-inch depth when a sandy loam will not form a ball if pressed in the hand; when a loam or silt loam balls, but is crumbly; and when a clay or clay loam is pliable but cracks appear in the ball. (A little experience is necessary to gain confidence in this method.)

3. Keep a weather balance record. This requires information on how much available water the soil can hold per foot of depth. If the Soil Conservation Service cannot provide this information, a grower can use the general figures on page101. It also calls for data on rainfall amounts, which can be established by keeping rain gauge records, and for daily water losses through evaporation and transpiration.

Using the rainfall records and estimated daily loss information, a grower can estimate the water balance in his field and plan to irrigate when about one-half of the available water in the root zone is gone. This is a general guide, but it still pays to watch the crop for any indications of moisture stress.

It is best to saturate at least one foot of a silt clay soil and two feet of a sandy soil.

Irrigation Methods

Flooding, furrow irrigation, and overhead sprinkling are the commonly used methods of irrigating field crops. Local conditions usually dictate the use of a specific method. Research workers are investigating the feasibility of subsurface irrigation of field crops. This is accomplished by burying perforated plastic pipe or tubing below the plow depth. The University of Delaware reported promising results for this method. In 1968, Delmar soybeans produced 33 bushels more per acre than nonirrigated soybeans when 10 inches of water was applied through subsurface irrigation.

Good Drainage Is Needed

Good drainage is required for successful soybean production in humid areas. There is always the possibility of a heavy rain soon after irrigating. Too much water will cause ponding and flooding, and may increase losses from disease.

Discomfort Index

Temperature alone is not a good measure of a man's discomfort on a hot day. When humidity is low, he

13

does not notice the heat so much because evaporating perspiration keeps his skin cool. On a very humid day, there is little evaporational cooling. The term "discomfort index" is often used to describe how uncomfortable a man gets on hot days with varying relative humidity.

The discomfort index of plants is different from that of people. It is highest on clear, bright days with low relative humidity. This is because the rate of water lost from the leaves is inversely related to humidity. On bright days with low humidity, transpiration may exceed the rate of water uptake and translocation, hence the plant wilts. Wilting is one of the plant's mechanisms (closing stomata is the other) for reducing the loss of water and thus tolerating heat and drouth. A wilted plant presents less surface to the sun than a turgid plant.

13. Poor drainage is a major factor limiting crop yields in some areas. A soybean disease, phytophthora rot, often prevails in low, poorly drained areas.

6

Weed Control

1

Soybeans are not strong weed competitors in the early part of the season. Some weeds may outgrow them. This often results in special weed control problems. Until soybean-safe postemergence herbicides are developed to control both broadleaf weeds and grasses, good weed control will continue to require planning and timely operations.

The grower should check with local dealers and extension agents annually for information on available herbicides. To make wise use of any of these materials, he must have an understanding of the principles of weed control.

Kill Weeds Early

Research at the University of Illinois and Iowa State University shows that weed competition is not a serious threat to soybean yields if the weeds are removed by the time the soybeans reach the flowering stage. This might suggest that early weed control is not important. If there were a sure and economical post-emergence method of killing weeds without damaging the crops, this might be true. But currently used control methods are more effective and economical on small weeds than large ones. Therefore, soybean weed control practices in most cases should be concentrated in the early part of the season.

Early season control is especially important because weeds, if left after midseason, seriously affect yields. In some seasons, a pound of soybean dry matter (weight of stems, leaves, and beans) may be lost

1. **Many weeds that emerge with soybeans increase in height at about the same rate as the crop. For this reason, and also because weeds are killed most easily in the early growth stages, early season control is important.**

for every pound of weed dry matter produced. In other situations the ratio is not so great. However, maximum yields are not possible when weeds are prevalent.

Weeds that germinate after the crop shades the ground may not survive. If they do live, they usually affect yield only to the extent that they contribute to harvest loss.

2

2. Young giant foxtail plants that emerge and grow with soybeans offer strong competition and reduce crop yield.

Effect of removing foxtail from soybeans

Soybean height when foxtail was removed (inches)	Average yield (bushels per acre)
Weed-free check	30
8	30
12	30
16	29
22	28
Left until beans were mature	12

University of Illinois

Shading suppresses foxtail in soybeans

Time foxtail was seeded after crop was planted	Total dry matter produced (pounds per acre)	
	Foxtail	Soybeans
Same day	2,280	3,970
3 weeks	30	5,240
6 weeks	0	5,390
12 weeks	0	5,440
Weed-free	0	5,410

University of Illinois

Days after planting before canopy covers inter-row area

Row width (inches)	Number of days
40	67
30	58
20	47
10	36

University of Nebraska

3. Row spacing is related to weed control in several respects. If cultivation is required to control weeds, the farmer using 40-inch rows (directly below) will have an easier job than the one using 30-inch rows (next right) or the one who has planted in 20-inch rows (far right). When rows are narrowed from 40- to 20-inch spacing, the job of cultivation not only becomes more difficult, but the linear feet of row per acre doubles. Narrow-row soybeans do contribute to weed control by providing earlier shade of the inter-row area (table, right).

3

  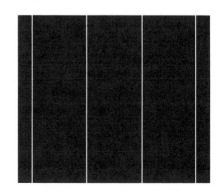

4. Two plots photographed the same day in July at the University of Illinois present a vivid contrast. The soybeans in 40-inch rows (left) have not yet covered the inter-row area. Soybeans of the same variety in 20-inch rows (right) shade the inter-row space, providing some control of weeds starting from late-germinating seed.

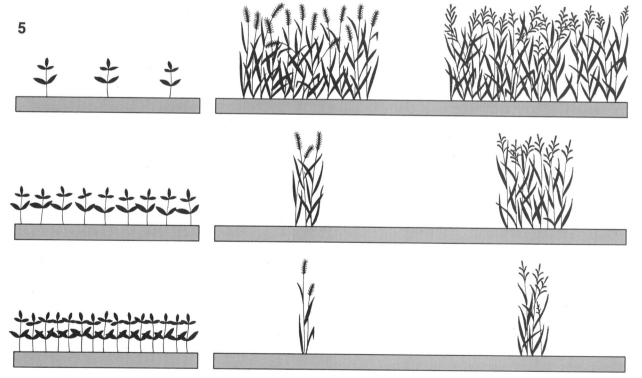

5. A thin stand of soybeans favors a heavy population of weeds in the crop row. The relative populations of giant foxtail and smartweed plants are shown for stands of 3, 9, and 15 soybean plants per foot of row. In an effort to get a measure of the value of crop shading, researchers used no herbicide in these comparison plots.

6

7

8

6. The rotary hoe is highly effective in removing weed seedlings from stands of soybeans. It flips the tiny, shallow-rooted weeds from the soil without disturbing the deeper rooted seedling soybeans.

Plant in Narrow Rows

Unfortunately, narrow rows do not contribute to early season weed control. In fact, they may complicate mechanical control, because narrow rows are difficult to cultivate. In addition, there are more linear feet of row per acre in narrow rows. However, the leaf canopy of narrow row soybeans covers the area between rows more quickly than that of soybeans in 36- to 40-inch rows. Once the canopy is developed, the shade is quite dense. Late-germinating weeds such as giant foxtail, which are not shade-tolerant, do poorly or die. Even the more shade-tolerant weeds seem to lose vigor.

The Value of Good Seed

Good seed makes a major contribution to weed control, especially if planted in a well-prepared seedbed and at a uniform depth. Under these conditions, the grower can expect a uniform stand of vigorous seedlings to help shade out the early and late-season weeds. Also, fast-growing seedlings get a headstart, providing the necessary height differential for effective use of cultivation or directed postemergence spray. Most directed sprays are nonselective herbicides that kill small weeds in the row. It is important that the herbicide-soybean contact be minimized.

7. The disk harrow is an effective implement for controlling weeds before planting, or for use in summer fallowing for weed control. These techniques may cause the loss of precious soil moisture before planting.

8. Weeds this small or smaller are controlled effectively by rotary hoeing. Larger weeds may survive the treatment.

9. Sweep cultivators have retained a place of importance in soybean weed control. Where pre-emergence herbicide is applied in bands, cultivators are used to keep the inter-row areas weed-free until the crop produces shade.

A good stand also aids weed control by shading out weeds in the row. Iowa State researchers report that weed population increases as the number of soybean plants per foot of row decreases. Good seed quality and uniform planting depth help to give uniform stands free of gaps.

Some herbicides may depress soybean growth early in the season (Chapter 7). Vigorous seedlings are most likely to outgrow these effects. The use of good seed and selection of optimum planting depth affect seedling vigor. Seedlings from deep-planted seed grow more slowly in their early life than those from seed planted only 1 to 1½ inches deep.

It is also important to use disease-resistant varieties. Herbicide injury may aggravate crop disease injury. This is especially true of diseases that attack the root system, such as phytophthora.

Crop Rotation

Rotating crops — and, therefore, herbicides — often enables the grower to match the herbicide or mechanical control method to a specific weed problem. For example, one way to reduce a cocklebur or morning glory problem is to plant the field to corn, using postemergence 2,4-D spray. Soybeans can be planted the following year with less cocklebur or morning-glory troubles.

Two other examples are the control of Johnsongrass and quackgrass:

— In the southern soybean area, the rhizomes of established Johnsongrass are killed by summer fallow or a combination of summer fallow and herbicides following the harvest of fall-planted small grain.

— In the northern soybean area, established quackgrass is killed by fall application of atrazine. Since soybeans are susceptible to this chemical, corn is the first crop grown after treatment. After the quackgrass population has been removed, re-establishment of the weed pest from seed can usually be prevented by using appropriate soybean pre-emergence herbicides.

Mechanical Weed Control Measures

Disking or harrowing before planting: There is little advantage to disking or harrowing more than once before planting to kill annual weeds. A possible exception to this rule is the case where there is a danger that the weeds will get too large to be killed easily. Disking kills the crop of weeds that is growing but it also brings ungerminated weed seed to the surface. Also, in some areas, it causes the loss of precious soil moisture.

If perennial weeds are the problem, they should be allowed to grow one or two weeks before disking. The early weed growth is made at the expense of food reserves stored in the roots. Killing the top growth of the small perennial weed will weaken its reserves.

Rotary hoeing: The rotary hoe is a very good weed control tool for use in soybeans. Success with this

115

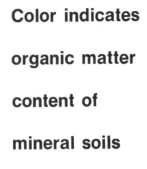

10

Color indicates

organic matter

content of

mineral soils

Average organic matter 5%

Average organic matter 3½%

This page is a guide for estimating the organic matter content of soils in selecting herbicide rates.

1. Take a sample from the plow layer.
2. Use moist soil — neither wet nor dry. If the sample is dry, moisten it.
3. Find which color block matches most closely the soil color.
4. Read the associated organic matter content.

The most accurate estimates are obtained with medium- and fine-textured soils. Soils containing high proportions of sand (more than 50 percent) and low proportions of clay (less than 10 percent) usually contain less organic matter than indicated by this method.

Organic soils, such as mucks and peats, contain 20 to 90 percent organic matter. Mucks are normally black and soft, while peats tend to be brown and fibrous. This color key is not intended to apply to organic soils.

For more information about soils contact the College of Agriculture or local extension agent or vo-ag instructor.

This page based on contents of a publication of the University of Illinois Cooperative Extension Service.

Average organic matter 2½%

Average organic matter 2%

Average organic matter 1½%

implement depends primarily on timeliness and speed of operation. The best time to use the rotary hoe is after weed seeds have germinated but before the majority of the weeds have emerged. The weeds must be very small to be controlled successfully by this implement. The objective is to throw the shallow-rooted weed out of the ground or to disturb the soil around it enough to interfere seriously with water uptake.

The seedling soybeans, which are more deeply rooted than the weeds, are not damaged severely by the rotary hoe. Soybeans should be allowed to lose their early morning turgidity before rotary hoeing begins. A bright, warm day also improves the effect of hoeing by increasing the wilting of the weeds.

Sweep cultivation: When cultivation is necessary to control weeds, the cultivator should be set to run shallow. This is particularly true after the soybeans are 8 to 10 inches tall. The majority of the soybean roots are in the surface 12 inches of the soil. Dr. R. L. Mitchell of Iowa State University reports that lateral roots under Iowa conditions reach the center of 30-inch rows within five to six weeks after planting.

Chemical Weed Control

Where there is a potential weed problem, crop planning should include a combination of chemical and mechanical control. Chemical control may start with a preplant application of a pre-emergence herbicide. Preplant herbicides are normally broadcast and

11. Soil-incorporated herbicides are handled in various ways. One popular system is to mount a boom sprayer and spray tanks on a tractor pulling a disk harrow. In one trip over the field, the herbicide is applied and incorporated. On some soils, incorporated herbicides may be applied in the fall, eliminating a job the following spring.

12. Some pre-emergence herbicides are best adapted for band application at the time of planting. This applicator, distributed by one herbicide manufacturer, dispenses herbicide concentrate, eliminating the conventional spray rig and the job of diluting chemicals with water.

worked into the soil before planting. Some are volatile and will be lost if left on the surface. Some are photosensitive and must be protected from the effect of the sun. Such herbicides, therefore, need to be incorporated with the soil to prevent rapid degradation and loss.

Incorporated herbicides are usually less dependent on rainfall after application than those applied on the surface. The success of both types of chemicals is influenced by such factors as soil type, soil moisture, and rainfall.

The effectiveness of some herbicides is influenced by the organic matter content of the soil. As a result of this, an application rate that causes crop injury in one field may fail to control weeds elsewhere. There is a high degree of correlation between the organic matter content and color of the soil. Professor John Alexander at the University of Illinois developed a color code to aid in adjusting herbicide application

13. The self-propelled, high-clearance spray rig is useful in making post-emergence herbicide applications, especially when large acreages are to be covered.

14. The coffeebean is a tall-growing annual weed that infests soybean fields in southern areas. This weed, which towers 6 to 10 feet tall at maturity is resistant to many of the commonly used herbicides.

13

14

rates to the soil type. While the code was developed for Illinois, it can be used to estimate the organic content of most soils in the soybean production area. The color blocks appear on page 116.

The soybean grower should check the performance of his pre-emergence herbicide often, regardless of whether it is incorporated or surface applied. If there is any doubt about the effectiveness, supplemental control measures can be used. If the weeds are small enough to be controlled by the rotary hoe, there is no reason to avoid using this implement. Rotary hoeing will not seriously reduce the effectiveness of most pre-emergence herbicides. Other measures to supplement chemical weed control may include cultivation, postemergence herbicide, flame cultivation, or any combination of these.

Postemergence Herbicides

There are several postemergence herbicides for use in soybeans. Most of them are more effective on broadleaf weeds than annual grasses. The labels of postemergence herbicides give specific warnings on preventing or limiting crop contact. The crop can tolerate some herbicides, but only if they are kept off the leaves and if they strike only the base of the stem. Carefully operated equipment is needed for the application of these directed sprays.

A few herbicides, such as 2,4-DB, may be sprayed over the crop. Crop damage sometimes results, however, since soybeans are not highly tolerant to these

herbicides. It is usually the practice to reserve use of these chemicals to problem fields or spot treatments of problem areas.

Aerial Application of Herbicides

Aerial application of herbicides is increasing. This is particularly true in some southern areas where fields are large and dinitro is applied at the "cracking stage" (as the soybeans are just breaking through the soil). The main advantage for aerial application is timeliness. Not only can application be made regardless of soil conditions, but a large acreage can be treated in a short time. However, there is the obvious danger of drift. Also, few herbicides are well adapted to aerial application. For example, those that require incorporation into the soil soon after application can be applied by plane, but the relative slowness of the incorporation equipment still limits the total acres treated per hour. Nevertheless, aerial application is used on large delta plantations where several tractors pulling disks 20 or more feet wide incorporate the chemical in short order. Aerially applied postemergence herbicides must be soybean safe.

2,4-D Wax Bars

The 2,4-D wax bar is used in the South to control the tall-growing coffeebean weed. The technique is to suspend the wax bar two or three inches above crop level. As the implement moves through the field, the bar rubs against the weeds, missing the crop.

15

15. Coffeebeans are controlled by the use of 2, 4-D wax bars. The bars should be attached to a tractor boom and suspended two to three inches above the top of the soybeans. As the unit moves through the field, the bar drags against the weeds (left), coating them with 2, 4-D. The weeds soon show the effect of the chemical (lower left).

Flame Cultivation

Flame cultivation, used by some growers in controlling cottonfield weeds, has limited application in soybean production. Soybeans are not as well adapted to this method because the stems of small plants lack the toughness to withstand the high temperature. By the time the soybeans are large enough and tough enough to be flame cultivated the weeds are often too large to be killed easily. A new principle, involving forced air to blow the leaves up and out of the way of the flame and also to cool the soybean plant, has been tested at Iowa State University.

New Weed Control Methods

New methods of applying chemical herbicides are being sought. In the late sixties, researchers at the Delta Branch Experiment Station experimented with foams to carry postemergence herbicides. Use of the foam resulted in more herbicide getting on the weeds than in the case of directed postemergence sprays. Also, the foam helped to keep the weeds moist, increasing the control effectiveness of the herbicide. Some problems, such as the need to find an ideal foaming agent, remained to be solved as this book went to press.

Handling Herbicides

While many soybean herbicides are not highly toxic to humans and animals, all should be handled with care, and used according to label instructions. Some

16. New ideas in applying herbicides are tested constantly. One technique given recent attention is the use of foam to carry postemergence herbicides.

17. Flame weeding has been used by some soybean growers. The soybean, however, seems to be more susceptible to heat damage than some other crops. Sometimes weeds get out of hand before the crop can tolerate the heat of flaming.

16

17

herbicides are irritating to the skin and eyes. All should be stored in a safe container out of the reach of children and livestock.

Most of the oil and a fair amount of the solid part of the soybean finds its way into human food. The restrictions concerning chemical residue in the plant are very strict, and the presence of contaminants makes the crop legally unfit for food or feed. Occasionally a herbicide may be cleared for use only in seed production fields. In such a case, the chemical must not be used on beans intended for use as food or feed.

Changing the Weed Infestation

The use of effective herbicides can cause a marked change in the weed problems of an area. If, for example, grasses are the major weed pests and grass-killing herbicides are used for several consecutive years, the grass may eventually decline while some broadleaf weeds increase in importance. For this reason, a grower should check his fields carefully to detect new weeds or weeds which seem to be increasing in number.

Cultivation Without Weeds

Early research indicated that the only reason for cultivating was to control weeds. If there were no weeds, there was no reason to stir the soil. More recent research contradicts this theory. Where weeds are controlled by herbicides, the soil surface often develops

a very tough crust in the absence of cultivation. The breaking of this crust has proven beneficial to yield.

Biological Weed Control

Scientists are searching for biological weed killers, such as insects or diseases. The examples of success in this area are few. However, progress is being made. In 1969, the USDA announced the discovery of a compound made by the bacteria *Rhizobium japonicum* that kills several weed species. The interesting part of the report is that the strains of Rhizobium capable of making the compound were first found in nodules on a soybean plant.

18

18. Johnsongrass is one of the more serious weeds infesting soybean fields, particularly in parts of the South. The weed grows from seed and rhizomes.

19. Annual morning glory is a troublesome pest of soybean fields. If this pest escapes control measures and remains in the crop until maturity, the twining stems make combining difficult and contribute to harvest losses.

21

19

20

21. Corn, a common weed pest in midwestern soybeans, is a greater problem than most growers realize. The corn plants compete with soybeans for water and nutrients. Kernels are classed as a contaminate in soybeans.

22. The pigweed, often called carelessweed or redroot, is a broadleafed annual. It is controlled by several of the major herbicides. Small, spiny flowers arise in fingerlike clusters from bases of leaf stalks and ends of branches.

22

20. Giant foxtail is a major pest of the soybean field, particularly in the Midwest, when it emerges with and grows alongside the crop. If left until soybeans mature, giant foxtail may reduce yields by 50 to 60 percent, or more.

23

23. Quackgrass is one of the more troublesome grasses infesting midwestern and northern soybean fields. It is a perennial that has underground roots which send out new stems at each joint or node. The roots extend up to eight feet in length, causing dramatic spread of the weed.

24. The cocklebur, a broadleaf annual that may grow four feet or more in height, has a self perpetuation feature. Each prickly bur contains two seed, one which will germinate the spring following maturity, and another which often germinates a year later.

24

7

Troubleshooting

Soybeans are beset by an increasing number of pests. The problem is complicated by the fact that some infestations are spreading. For example, the disease brown stem rot, once confined to the central Corn Belt, is now found almost everywhere in the northern production region and in some areas of the South.

Most insects that now trouble soybeans were originally pests of other plants. They simply developed an appetite for soybeans as the crop acreage increased. An example is the weed borer, which traditionally feeds on ragweed, horseweed, and other weeds. It was found feeding on soybeans for the first time in 1968.

The diseases, insects, nutrient deficiencies, and herbicide injuries of soybeans described in this chapter may or may not affect crop profits. The grower, however, should know how to identify all crop troubles. There are both reasons and methods for treating some of them.

It usually is easy to determine if the trouble is caused by an insect, a disease, or something else. Often, the difficult problem is identifying the pest specifically. There are some look-a-like troubles. A crinkled, thickened leaf, for example, is the symptom of both 2,4-D damage and soybean mosaic. A careful examination of the pattern of damage and its location reveals distinguishing characteristics of the two.

Some problems occur irregularly — appearing one year, then returning two or three years later. This is primarily because insects and diseases respond to the environment. Under some conditions they will increase rapidly; under others, they may present no serious threat to the crop. In addition, the growth stage and/or condition of the plant may determine whether treatment is justified. Leaf feeding by insects after pods have begun to fill is more serious than that before the flowering stage is reached. Similarly, disease infection or insect feeding may be of greater concern when the crop is under moisture stress than when it is growing vigorously.

This chapter includes five sections:

— Soybean troubles through the season
— Diseases of soybeans
— Insects of soybeans
— Soybean nutrient deficiencies
— Miscellaneous soybean troubles

Soybean Troubles Through the Season

On the next two pages is a list of soybean troubles in approximate order of their occurrence during the season. The exact timing of a disease or insect infestation, of course, cannot be predicted accurately. In addition, there is considerable overlapping. For instance, the disease phytophthora rot may be severe any time from seed germination until the plant is mature. The various crop ailments are categorized in three stages.

Various Soybean Crop Ailments

Symptom: Skips in the row where plants failed to emerge

Causes: Planter failure (clogged planter plate, etc.); soil too dry (seed normal size, not swelled); soil too cold or too wet (seed swelled but not sprouted or with small sprout only)

Symptom: Rotted seed or seedling

Causes: Pythium rot, page 128
Fusarium rot, page 128
Phytophthora rot, page 131

Symptom: Hypocotyl twisted, mis-shapened, or thickened underground

Causes: Herbicide injury, page 147
Soil crust or compacted soil, page 148

Symptom: Seed eaten or sprout cut off

Causes: Seed corn maggot, page 136
Wireworm, page 137
Seed corn beetle, page 137

Stage 2
Seedling to Flowering

Symptom: Plants wilted or dead in small areas or by individual plants
Causes: Rhizoctonia rot, pages 128
Fusarium root rot, page 128
Anthracnose, page 128
Phytopthora rot, page 131
Lesser cornstalk borer, page 138
Lightning damage, page 148

Symptom: Plants stunted, leaves discolored; some plants may die
Causes: Soybean cyst nematode, page 133
Root-knot nematode, page 135
Sting nematode, page 135
White grub, page 137
Lesser cornstalk borer, page 138
Grape colaspis, page 137
Garden symphylans, page 138
Herbicide injury, page 147

Symptom: Plants stunted, leaves thickened and possibly discolored
Causes: Soybean mosaic, page 129
Bud blight, page 131
Nutrient deficiencies, page 144
Herbicide injury, page 147

Symptom: Plants normal height, leaves discolored
Causes: Bacterial blight, 129
Brown spot, page 130
Bacterial pustule, page 130
Wildfire, page 131
Downy mildew, page 131
Phyllosticta leaf spot, page 130
Nutrient deficiencies, page 144

Symptom: Plants normal height, evidence of insect feeding
Causes: Thrips, page 137
Southern corn rootworm, page 138
Bean leaf beetle, page 138
Clover leaf weevil and clover root curculio, page 138
Grasshopper, page 140
Japanese beetle, page 138

Stage 3
Flowering to Maturity

Symptom: Plants normal height, leaves discolored
Causes: Anthracnose, page 128
Bacterial pustule, page 130
Downy mildew, page 131

Symptom: Plants normal height, leaves show evidence of insect feeding
Causes: Japanese beetle, page 138
Grasshopper, page 140
Two-spotted spider mite, page 140
Three-cornered alfalfa hopper, page 140
Mexican bean beetle, page 141
Cabbage looper, page 142
Garden webworm, page 142
Velvet bean caterpillar, page 142
Corn earworm, page 142
Stink bug, page 143

Symptom: Plants die prematurely (in the northern region mature plants retain dead leaves)
Causes: Brown stem rot, page 132
Southern blight , page 131
Phytophthora rot, page 131
Stem canker, page 131
Pod and stem blight, page 132
Charcoal rot, page 131
Lightning damage, page 148

Symptom: Plants remain green after remainder of the field matures
Causes: Bud blight, page 131
Herbicide injury, page 147

Symptom: Pods show evidence of insect feeding, leaf feeding usually is evident
Causes: Grasshopper, page 140
Mexican bean beetle, page 141
Velvet bean caterpillar, page 142
Corn earworms, page 142
Stink bugs, page 143
Fall armyworm, page 143

Symptom: Pods and/or seeds abnormal in
Causes: Anthracnose, page 128
Downy mildew, page 131
Purple seed stain, page 133
Pod and stem blight, page 132
Stink bug, page 143

1. The plant at the far left is infected severely with Rhizoctonia rot. The next two plants are less severely affected. The plant on the right is healthy.

Diseases of Soybeans

About 50 diseases attack soybeans. In any given year some of these may be found almost anywhere soybeans are grown. Others are not so widespread through the production area, and still others require a rather specific environment before they can develop.

All soybean diseases inflict plant damage, but some, like phytophthora and the soybean cyst nematode are especially serious. Plant breeders are constantly searching for resistance and, in these two cases, it has been found. Use of resistant varieties is the most practical and economical means of controlling soybean diseases. Foliar or soil-applied fungicides and nematocides are usually too expensive for commercial soybean production.

Pythium rot. This disease attacks soybeans any time from seedling stage to midseason. In most of the production area it occurs early in the season because its development is favored by cold, wet soil. It may cause seed decay or kill the young seedling before or shortly after emergence. Outer stem tissues of older infected plants turn brown and slough off.

No control or resistant variety. Seed treatment will not control the disease but does give some protection against seed decay.

Rhizoctonia rot. Infection normally results in damping off or death of small soybean plants. The disease, favored by wet weather, often occurs in more or less circular patches up to 10 feet in diameter. Characteristic of the disease is a reddish-brown area of the main stem and upper root around the soil line. The symptom differs from that of Pythium in that this infected area is firm. That of Pythium is soft. Rhizoctonia is not easily distinguished from phytophthora in the field. The area infected by phytophthora is normally dark brown without the reddish cast associated with Rhizoctonia. Rhizoctonia is seldom a problem past the small plant stage. Phytophthora, on the other hand, remains a killer all season long. Rhizoctonia is most common in the Midwest. However, in certain areas in the South, the fungus under hot, humid conditions attacks soybeans and causes a buff to dark brown spotting of the leaves.

No control or resistant variety. Seed treatment not effective.

Fusarium root rot. This seedborne disease occurs in scattered fields throughout the soybean producing area. Its root rot phase is most frequently observed on seedlings or young plants. Later, the same disease may attack older plants, causing a wilting under dry conditions. Heavy rain, flooding, and a compacted soil apparently favor this disease.

No control or resistant variety. Seed treatment not effective.

Anthracnose. This minor disease of soybeans is found throughout the soybean producing area. It may contribute to poor stands. Seeds infected with the disease either do not germinate or the weakened seedlings die. Late season attacks are favored by rainy periods.

2. Soybean mosaic

2

No control or resistant variety. Crop rotation, use of disease free seed, and plowing under crop residue help avoid the disease.

Soybean mosaic. This disease of minor importance may occur wherever soybeans are grown. Infected plants are stunted and have crinkly or ruffled leaves. The leaf blades are puckered along the veins and the margins turn down. Pods, when affected, contain fewer seeds than usual. Most varieties outgrow the symptoms when temperatures reach or exceed the middle 80's. The symptoms of this disease may be confused with 2,4-D damage. However, 2,4-D damage normally occurs along the edges of a field, and is more uniformly distributed than a disease.

No control or resistant variety. Seed from infected plants should not be saved for planting.

Bacterial blight. This disease, found throughout the soybean producing area, is one of the earliest leaf spots to appear on young plants. The infected area is small and angular, and its center is yellow to brown. The center is surrounded by a water-soaked margin. The spots eventually dry, turn brown, and become sunken. Several spots may run together. The dead tissue often falls from the leaf; subsequent whipping by the wind tears the damaged leaf, giving it a ragged appearance. Bacterial blight may be observed any time during the season. It is favored by cool weather and frequent rain or dew.

No control or resistant variety. The disease is seed-borne and it overwinters in dead leaves. Therefore,

3. Bacterial blight

3

4. Brown spot

4

5. Bacterial pustule

5

seed should not be saved from badly infected fields, nor should soybeans follow a badly infected crop.

Brown spot. This early appearing disease is often found on the first true or unifoliate leaves. The diseased areas are angular and reddish to chocolate-brown in color. They range up to about one-fifth inch in diameter. The diseased area on the underside of the leaf often has a pronounced reddish-brown color. This is particularly true on the unifoliate leaves. The absence of a water-soaked margin is one feature that distinguishes this disease from bacterial blight. Infected leaves turn yellow and drop prematurely. This defoliation progresses upward during the season, and a heavily infected plant may lose half its leaves.

No control or resistant variety. Crop rotation may reduce the severity of this disease since it overwinters on diseased leaves and stems. Plowing under crop residue also helps avoid the disease.

Bacterial pustule. This warm-weather disease usually is seen later than brown spot or bacterial blight. In the Corn Belt it usually appears in mid-July or later. At first, the infected area is a yellow-green spot with a reddish-brown center which is most conspicuous on the upper leaf surface. The center portion of the spot appears slightly raised and develops into a small pustule. This is most easily seen on the underside of the leaf. A heavily infected leaf develops large yellow-to-brown areas dotted with small, darker brown spots. As the leaf tissue dies, the leaves tear and break up and are ragged in appearance. Late stages of this dis-

ease are not easily distinguished from those of bacterial blight. However, in the early stages of development the disease is distinguished by a lack of water-soaked area around the infected spots.

Resistant varieties available.

Wildfire. This disease is easily identified by the prominent yellow halo around the central area of brown, dead leaf tissue. It occurs only where bacterial pustule is found. The wildfire bacteria invade areas already infected by bacterial pustule. In damp weather the infected spots enlarge and run together. The disease may cause considerable loss of leaves.

Plant varieties resistant to bacterial pustule.

Phyllosticta leaf spot. This leaf disease, less common than some of those already listed, may severely defoliate young plants. Lesions normally form first near the margin of the leaf as round, oval, or indefinitely shaped, dull gray spots. Later, the spots may be tan with a dark brown border. The disease normally appears in early season and is seldom observed on plants that have passed the third and fourth leaf stage.

No control or resistant variety.

Target spot. Most southern varieties are resistant to this disease, and it has not been especially serious in the northern production area. Target spot, which usually attacks the leaves, may also attack the petioles, stems, and pods. Reddish-brown spots occur on the leaves, sometimes forming concentric rings of dead tissue. The infected areas start as very small spots and may increase to one-half inch or more in di-

6

6. The leaf on the left is from a plant affected by wildfire; the leaf on the right is from a healthy plant.

ameter. Spots on the stems and petioles are dark brown, varying greatly in size. Infected areas on pods are usually small and circular with purple-black centers that are slightly depressed.

Resistant varieties available.

Downy mildew. This disease is found throughout the soybean producing region. The infection is seed-borne. When infected seed is planted, the first leaves to unfold on the seedling are sometimes covered with mildew growth.

No control or resistant variety. Crop rotation, plowing under soybean crop residue, and the use of disease-free seed help avoid this disease.

Bud blight. This pest of soybeans throughout the growing season causes young plants to be stunted, with a characteristic crook at the top of the stem. The terminal bud becomes brown and turns down, forming the crook. The leaf immediately below the terminal bud may show a flecking of rusty-brown spots. Plants infected before flowering may set few or no pods. They remain green after healthy plants have matured. The disease is only occasionally severe. It is usually noticed first on the edge of the field.

No control or resistant variety.

Phytophthora rot. A problem in most of the soybean producing area, this disease is especially serious in parts of Indiana and Ohio. It attacks soybeans of all ages. Newly emerged seedlings develop a soft rot of the stem, and die. Older plants turn yellow and the leaves wilt. A dark brown lesion usually forms on the

stems, near the base or several inches above the soil surface. Dark brown lesions form on the roots, too. This characteristic color may aid in distinguishing between Rhizoctonia and phytophthora early in the growing season. Rhizoctonia is seldom a problem after mid-July. Phytophthora usually kills just a few plants in a row, or only the plants in a low, poorly drained area of the field. However, in badly infected fields during wet seasons the disease may be more uniformly distributed, perhaps to the extent of causing the crop to be abandoned because of poor stand.

Resistant varieties available.

Charcoal rot. This minor disease is most likely to be observed in the South, late in the season, following hot, dry weather that retarded plant growth. It attacks the base of the stem and roots. Small black fruiting bodies (sclerotia) are found under the bark of the root and stem.

No control or resistant variety.

Southern blight (Sclerotial blight). This southern disease is largely confined to sandy soils. The dead plants have brown sclerotia on the stem near the base of the plant. The sclerotia are produced on a cottony mycelial growth.

No control or resistant variety. The residue from a diseased crop should be plowed under.

Stem canker. Occurring most commonly in the Midwest, this disease kills plants during the last half of the season. It may be identified by the brown, slightly sunken lesion (canker) that girdles the stem. The can-

9. Phytophthora rot

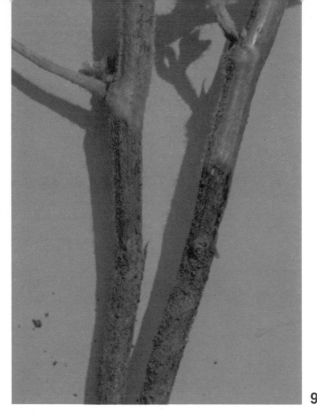

9

7. Downy mildew foliage symptom

7

8. Downy mildew seed symptom

8 ker is usually at the base of a branch or leaf petiole. The stem and leaves above the canker die. The dried up leaves remain attached to the dead plant.

Varieties differ in susceptibility.

Brown stem rot. First discovered in Illinois, this disease is found in most of the northern soybean production region, and has been reported in some southern areas. It attacks the plant relatively early in the season, but symptoms usually do not appear until later. Twenty to 30 days before normal maturity, the leaves of diseased plants may turn brown and dry rapidly. The tissue near the veins in these leaves remains green for a few days. If the disease is severe, the plants may lodge. The leaf symptoms do not always appear, so the best way to identify brown stem rot is to split the stem of suspected plants. A dark reddish-brown pith (instead of a healthy white) reveals infected plants.

Control: Rotate soybeans with other crops, allowing two or three years between crops of soybeans.

Pod and stem blight. This disease may be found wherever soybeans are grown. It appears late in the season and is favored by rain and high humidity. The fungus grows on the stems and pods. When infection is severe and the plant has been weakened by other diseases or unfavorable weather, it may be present on the seeds, causing them to be white. The identifying characteristic is black fruiting bodies called pycnidia, which are found on the pods and stems. On the stems these pycnidia are arranged in rows running

10. Charcoal rot

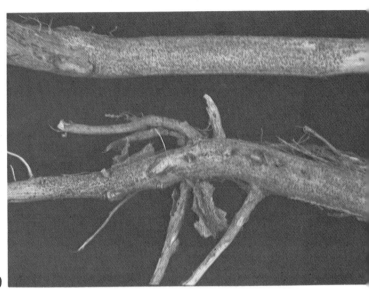

10

11

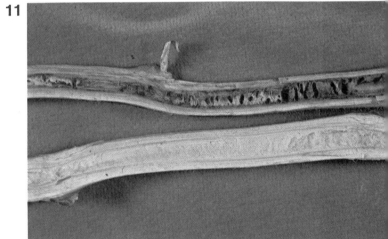

11. Brown stem rot

lengthwise of the stem.

No control or resistant variety.

Purple seed stain. This disease is sometimes referred to as Cercospora because it is caused by one or more species of the Cercospora fungus. The most common of these, *Cercospora kikuchii,* causes a purple discoloration of the seed. However, the organism also attacks other plant parts. Leaves of infected plants, for example, have small, angular, reddish-brown spots late in the season. These may coalesce to form large dead areas. The discolored areas on diseased seeds vary from pink to dark purple, and may be small or almost cover the seed. Cracks often occur in the discolored area. Seed may be downgraded in market value because of excessive purple stain. Seedlings that develop from diseased seed may die.

Control: Treat seed with fungicide; some varieties are tolerant. Use high-quality seed. Seed treatment does not prevent the disease from infecting the growing crop.

Soybean cyst nematode. This small, worm-like organism attacks soybean roots. It occurs on light and heavy soils. Heavily infected plants may start turning yellow within a month after planting. These will remain severely stunted throughout the growing season. The nematode damages the root tissue, reducing the uptake of water and nutrients. The damage occurs in more or less circular areas of the field, varying from only a few feet to 50 or more feet in diameter. Roots of infected plants are dark, and often have no nodules.

14. Purple seed stain

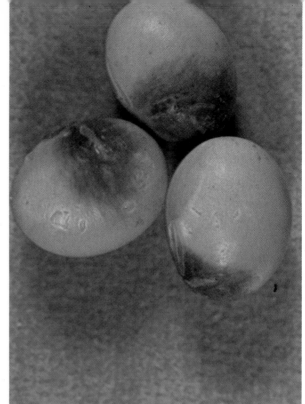

14

12. Pod and stem blight, showing pycnidia on the stem

12

13

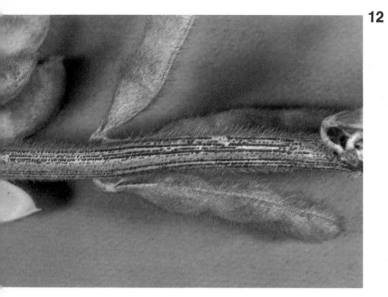

13. Pod and stem blight effect on seed

15

15. The cysts of the soybean cyst nematode are much larger than the tiny round nodules found on the roots of soybeans.

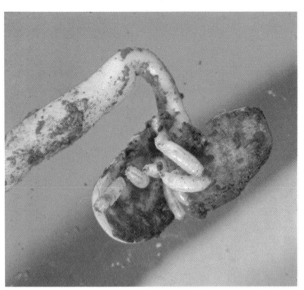

16. The gnarled galls caused by the root-knot nematode are easily recognized on the roots of a soybean plant.

Yields can be reduced severely.

Resistant varieties are available. Rotating the field to immune crops, such as corn, cotton, or sorghum, reduces the nematode population. A period of three to four years is required before soybeans can be grown again safely. Soil should not be moved from infested to nematode-free fields.

Root-knot nematode. The root galls caused by this pest are roughly spherical or elongated. They vary from very small swellings to galls two inches in diameter. The roots above the galls on severely infected plants are densely matted. The leaves of infected plants vary from light green to yellow. Plants may be stunted and wilt during dry weather before normal plants. Yields are often greatly reduced. Most soybean varieties are somewhat tolerant to the disease and may not show above-ground symptoms. The galls are usually distinguishable from the nodules. The nodules will break away from the root easily, the galls will not.

Control: Same as for soybean cyst nematode.

Sting nematode. This pest can be devastating. It kills plants in the seedling stage. Older plants are stunted and dull light green in appearance. Affected plants have stubby clusters of coarse, short roots.

No practical control. Rotation is difficult because of a wide range of host plants; fumigation is too ex-

pensive for economical soybean production.

Insects of Soybeans

Many insects attack soybeans, but relatively few can be considered economically serious pests. The constant progress in development and introduction of new insecticides makes it impractical to list specific chemicals here. Every soybean grower should stay in touch with local dealers and professional agricultural advisors to keep abreast of the progress in insect control.

Selecting an insecticide is only half of the decision that must be made in insect control. Equally important is the decision on whether treatment is practical. In some instances the peace of mind that comes from making a treatment may be worth the cost. In other situations, the decision rests on whether the potential economic loss is greater than the cost of chemicals and application.

There are ways to estimate the potential damage of many insects. In some cases the estimate is based on the insect population per foot of row. For some other insects, it is based on an estimate of the existing leaf damage. In both situations the stage of maturity of the insect is an important factor. A relatively low population of young worms carries more potential danger than a high population of mature worms. The presence of parasite and predator insects as well as diseases of the insects should be weighed in making the decision of whether to use chemical treatment.

18

18. Soil insecticides are used in controlling pests that attack planted seed and seedlings. These chemicals should be handled with care.

21. Wireworm

21

19. Slender seed corn beetle

20. Striped seed corn beetle

19 The population of many insects can be estimated by shaking the plants over the inter-row space covered by a strip of cloth or paper. This check should be made in several locations.

Under most conditions moderate defoliation early in the season has no appreciable effect on soybean yield. Therefore, the use of insecticides to control insects at this stage may not be practical unless the potential for serious defoliation is great. Fifty percent defoliation prior to flowering results in an average yield loss of only three percent.

As the soybean reaches the flowering and pod-filling stage, defoliation is a greater threat to yield. At these stages leaf-feeding insects warrant greater concern. A grower should consult entomologists in his **20** area for information on the amount of leaf feeding and the insect population at which treatment is warranted under local conditions.

Soybean insects may be classified as early, mid-, and late-season pests. Some of these occur in more than one part of the season, but are categorized here by the time of their greatest probable buildup.

Early-season insects

These insects attack seeds and seedlings.

Seed corn maggot. Planted seed are attacked by the larvae or maggots which are about one-fourth inch long, cylindrical, narrow in front, and large toward the posterior end. The damaged seed may not germinate.

22. **Thrips damage to soybean leaf** 22

Less-severely damaged seed that germinate may produce weak seedlings that die. Damage is usually scattered over the field but unless the population is high, the insect and its damage may go unnoticed. This insect is seldom a problem except when weather conditions or seed quality delay seedling emergence.

Since it is primarily a seed-eating insect, this pest can be controlled by seed treatment or use of a soil insecticide.

Seed corn beetle. The dark brown or tan adult (beetle) of this insect attacks the planted seed. Control is the same as for the seed corn maggot.

Wireworm. The larvae feed on planted seed and newly germinated seedlings. Damage may occur even after seedling emergence. The larva looks like a short piece of rusty wire. Mature wireworms are cream to dark brown in color, smooth, 1¼ to 1½ inch long, and about ⅛ inch in diameter. Damage is most likely in low-lying, poorly drained portions of the field. If the stand is partially destroyed and deciding whether to replant is difficult, the farmer can replant in the row middles. Then, because the wireworm does not migrate readily from row to row, one set of rows can be cultivated out.

Since the insect feeds on both the seed and the seedling, seed treatment is only partially effective. A soil-incorporated insecticide is the best control.

Grape colaspis. This insect attacks the roots of new seedlings almost as soon as they emerge. Pruning of the seedling roots restricts uptake of moisture and nutrients, causing the leaves to turn yellow. Under severe infestations the plants die. The possibility of grape colaspis damage is not great unless the previous soybean crop was infested or unless the soybeans follow another legume crop.

Soil-incorporated insecticides give good control.

White grub. Several species of this insect attack soybeans. They look alike but differ in life cycle. The true white grub is a serious pest on a three-year cycle. The annual white grub may be a problem more often. Damage is usually scattered in the field. Symptoms may vary from dead to stunted, yellow plants. The plants in the center of the infected area are often brown or dead; and those around the edges range from yellow to healthy green. Grubs are easily found in infected areas by digging in the row.

Since these root-feeding insects feed relatively deep in the soil, the only practical control is a soil insecticide.

Thrips. The full-grown adult, only 1/16 inch long, is yellow or black, depending on the species. The insects occasionally will migrate to a soybean field early in the season. They rasp the surface of the leaf and sponge up the sap through a tiny tube. Each feeding place is marked by a white spot. These form a longitudinal path or streak of tiny white spots. If the infestation is heavy and the weather dry, the field may take on a silvery cast. Heavily infected plants may be temporarily stunted. All effects disappear after a good rain.

23

24

Southern corn rootworm. (Spotted cucumber beetle). The adult beetle is ¼ to ⅜ inch long, yellow to green, and it has 11 black spots on its wing covers. It occasionally feeds on soybean leaves. It eats between the veins, leaving the leaf intact. Adult feeding is rarely important in soybeans; the larval, or worm stage, feeds on roots, and under certain circumstances may become a problem.

Lesser cornstalk borer. Serious damage from this insect is confined largely to the South, although it may be found further north. The bluish-green, brown-striped caterpillars feed first on the leaves, but soon burrow into the stems of small seedlings. Some of the plants die soon after attack, others are broken off by wind.

Control efforts are useless after damage has been observed. At this stage this pest is already inside the stalk, out of reach of the chemical. Best control is obtained from a soil insecticide applied before or at planting.

Bean leaf beetle. The adult beetle may feed on the stems of seedling plants at or just below the soil surface in early season. The larva, on the other hand, may attack the roots and nodules, or the base of the stem. Sometimes the larva girdles the base of the stem, contributing to lodging. The adult varies from reddish to yellow, and is ¼ inch or less in length. The larva is whitish in the middle and dark brown at both ends. The pest also damages the foliage, blossoms, and pods of soybeans.

Foliage-applied insecticides may be used to control the insect if the potential damage is of concern.

Cloverleaf weevil and clover root curculio. These insects seldom injure soybeans, except when they migrate from adjoining, freshly plowed clover fields or when soybeans follow clover. In the first situation, only the marginal rows may be damaged. In the second, damage may be found anywhere in the field. The larva of the cloverleaf weevil and the adult beetle of the clover root curculio are the stages that migrate to soybeans and feed on the leaves.

Seldom does either merit treatment.

Garden symphylans. This small, white centipede-like insect with long antennae may become 5/16 inch long. It moves rapidly and is difficult to catch. Only recently has this insect become a threat to crops. It prefers corn, but has been found feeding on the roots of soybeans in the Corn Belt. Feeding may begin almost as soon as the seed germinates. Seedlings with severely damaged roots wilt and die; less severe feeding causes stunting.

No control has been suggested.

Midseason insects

These insects attack plants from flowering through early pod formation.

Japanese beetle. Although not widespread in the soybean-producing area, this pest is very serious where it occurs. It feeds on soybean leaves and blossoms,

27. Japanese beetle

25. Cloverleaf weevil

25

27

26

28

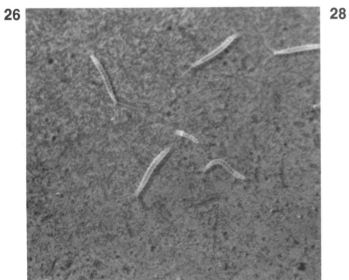

26. Garden symphlans

28. Grasshopper

31. Mexican bean beetle

29. Two-spotted spider mite

29

31

30

30. Three-cornered alfalfa hopper

and may leave the plant as a skeleton of leaf veins. The adult is a shiny, metallic green or greenish-bronze beetle about ⅓ to ½ inch long. It has reddish wing covers and two white spots at the tip of the abdomen.

Control measures should be discussed with local advisors.

Grasshopper. This universal pest is primarily a leaf feeder, but may also feed on pods. Grasshoppers are likely to migrate into soybean fields in July after depleting food supplies in fence rows and other uncropped areas. Since they fly in from other locations, grasshoppers first attack soybean plants at the edges of fields. This is where treatment should start if the population appears to be potentially harmful.

Two-spotted spider mite. All plant mites feed on the undersides of soybean leaves. Damage from this and other mites is first noticed at the edge of the field. The leaves are speckled or blotched with pale yellow and reddish brown spots. Undersides of the leaves appear dusty white. This is the result of a web spun by the mite. This pest is most serious during hot, dry weather.

Control is difficult because good coverage of the undersides of leaves with insecticide is essential.

Three-cornered alfalfa hopper. The triangular-shaped, light green insect feeds by piercing the stem near the base of the plant. Sometimes the punctures circle the stem, weakening it so badly that it lodges easily.

32

33

The application of insecticides is seldom warranted except on a spot treatment basis.

Late-season insects

These insects attack soybeans from podding to harvest.

Mexican bean beetle. Primarily a pest of garden beans, this insect is becoming a serious problem on soybeans in some areas. Both the adult and larva attack the soybean plant. The yellow to copper-colored adult is ¼ to ⅓ inch long. Each wing cover has eight black spots in three rows across the body. The larvae grow to ⅓ inch in length. They are oval-shaped, yellow, and have six rows of long-branching black-tipped spines on their backs. The adult beetle eats holes in leaves and pods. The larvae feed exclusively on the undersides of the leaves, leaving only the lace-like structure of the leaf veins. The Mexican bean beetle may be found on soybeans early in the season but the main buildup and damage usually occur in July or August.

Control is difficult because the larvae are on the undersides of the leaves and are not easily reached with sprays.

Blister beetles. There are several species of these insects resembling lightning bugs. The one most likely to be found feeding on soybeans is the striped blister beetle. It is about ¼ inch wide and ½ to ⅝ inch long, and is brown to gray with yellow stripes running the

33. Cabbage looper

34

35

length of the wing covers. Other species, ranging from gray to black, may be found on soybeans but normally feed on the pollen only. The striped blister beetle often migrates in large swarms and will suddenly appear in spots in a soybean field.

Chemical control is usually unnecessary.

Cabbage looper. The greenish larva or caterpillar is 1 to 1½ inches long when full-grown. It crawls with a characteristic humping of the body and a looping movement. Leaf feeding may result in plant defoliation if populations are heavy. Only occasionally is chemical control justified. Similar, but sometimes more serious pests in the South are the false cabbage looper and the spotted cabbage looper.

Green clover worm. The light green worm has two thin white stripes along each side of its body. It is from 1 to 1½ inches long. When disturbed, the worm drops to the ground and moves off rapidly with a looping or springing motion. Worms eat holes in the leaves and also feed on soybean blossoms. Leaves become ragged in appearance as the margins around the holes tear out. Parasites and diseases help keep the green clover worm under control.

Chemical control is required only when there is evidence of damage and a heavy buildup of small worms.

Garden and alfalfa webworm. These green to yellow insects are about one inch long when full-grown. They have black spots along their sides and bristle-like hairs project from these spots. They feed on the undersides of leaves in a light, silken web spun over the leaf and other plant parts. A parasitic wasp and disease helps keep these insects under control.

Chemical control may be needed occasionally when a heavy population of young worms occurs at the time pod filling is beginning.

Velvet bean caterpillar. Confined to the southern region, this caterpillar is about 1½ inches long. It varies from brownish-black to dull green. Several light-colored stripes run the length of its body, and its head is greenish-yellow to orange. Worms feed on both leaves and young pods. When numerous, they are capable of defoliating an area completely, and they cause many young pods to drop from the plant. The pest is very active when disturbed. It usually appears in late August, normally later than the corn earworm and the cabbage looper.

Chemical treatment may be warranted.

Corn earworm (bollworm). Found throughout the soybean-producing area, this pest is most serious in the southern region. It may reach a length of 1½ inches when mature. Color varies from light green to pink to almost black. Alternating light and dark stripes run the length of its body. The corn earworm feeds on foliage of the soybean plant, but the major damage results from pod feeding. If attacked, small pods either drop from the plant or fail to develop properly; holes are eaten in large pods.

Chemical treatment may be necessary, especially if worms ¼ to ½ inch long are numerous when the

36. Corn earworm

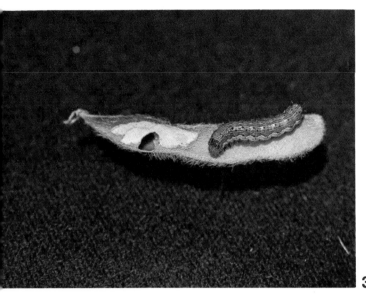

36

37

38

beans in the pods are small.

Stink bugs. At least three species of stink bugs attack soybeans late in the season. Serious damage is most likely to occur in the South, but economic losses from this pest have occurred as far north as St. Louis. The nymphs (young stink bugs) and the adults may be found on the same plant, and both feed on the soybean pods. These insects have sucking mouth parts. They damage the soybean seed by piercing the bean inside the pod. If the pod is young and the beans very small, further development may stop. If so, the pod will drop to the ground. Larger pods will remain on the plant, but the pierced beans will be shrunken, wrinkled, and discolored around the puncture. Badly damaged beans may be downgraded. Stink bug damage is objectionable in soybeans intended for export.

Chemical control is seldom needed on a field basis. Sometimes treatment of the field margins is desirable.

Fall army worm. The moth stage of this southern insect flies north each summer to feed on soybeans and other crops. The worm varies from green to nearly black. It has three yellowish-white hairlines down its back and on its sides. Next to the yellow lines is a wider dark stripe. Next to this is a somewhat waxy yellow stripe dotted with red. The insect may be distinguished from the true army worm by a prominent inverted Y on the front of its head. The mature worm is about 1 to 1½ inches long. The fall army worm feeds on both leaves and pods. Normally, the damage caused by this insect is not considered serious.

38. Stinkbug-damaged seed (immediately above) show the symptoms of yeast spot disease, a fungus carried by the insect. Normal seed (top) provide a vivid contrast.

39

40

39. Fall armyworm

40. Weed borer

41. Potassium deficiency

41

Weed borer. This versatile pest, which normally feeds on ragweed and other common weeds, attacked soybeans for the first time in southeastern Missouri during 1968. The adult beetle lays eggs in the top of the plant. The larvae that hatch burrow down inside the stem. About two inches above the ground they stop to girdle the inside of the stem, then continue downward. The first indication of the presence of the worm is when the girdled plants break off.

Soybean Nutrient Deficiencies

Nutrient deficiencies may be confused with symptoms of plant disease. Recognizing the difference, which is not always easy, is important because a nutrient deficiency can often be corrected. Identifying the deficiency requires complete information about previous soil treatment. In addition, the results of a soil test and plant analysis may be needed to make a positive diagnosis. The following summarizes the obvious nutrient deficiencies of soybeans. Full details on soybean fertility appear in Chapter 4.

Potassium deficiency. Soybeans exhibit symptoms of potassium deficiency readily. The first indication is an irregular yellow mottling around the edges of the leaflets. These chlorotic areas soon form a continuous, irregular yellow border. This tissue may die. If the deficiency is severe, only the center and base of the leaf will remain green. The symptom appears first on old leaves. The deficiency, most common on sandy, weathered, and highly organic soils, also may be found

on soils restricting roots by wetness or hardpan. If plants are small when the symptoms are noticed, side-dressing 50 to 60 pounds of K_2O, two to four inches from the row, may be tried in a small area. To avoid problems in the next crop, potassium should be broadcast according to the needs indicated by soil test.

Iron deficiency. New leaves early in the season turn yellow between the veins, which remain green. In extreme deficiencies, the tissue between the veins dries and drops out of the leaf. Plant growth is depressed. The deficiency is limited to soils high in pH. Some varieties, such as Wayne and Hark, are less able to utilize low levels of iron than others. They show iron deficiency under conditions that others, such as Harosoy 63, do not. The deficiency is favored by alkaline soils; wet, poorly aerated soils; compacted soils and cool weather. A trial suggestion for treatment is to spray the crop with a one percent solution of iron sulfate. Results have been inconsistent. Iron chelates have not been very effective either, but may be tried according to manufacturers' instructions. Use of non-susceptible varieties helps avoid this problem.

Manganese deficiency. Light green to white mottling between tne leaf veins is the symptom of manganese deficiency. The veins remain green until the chlorosis nears the white stage, then they also lose their color and the entire leaf may drop from the plant. This deficiency cannot be distinguished from iron deficiency.

42. Iron deficiency

42

45. Zinc deficiency

45

43. Manganese deficiency

43

46

46. Manganese toxicity

44

44. Petiole collapse caused by calcium deficiency

145

47. Boron toxicity

48. Amiben damage

47

48

It occurs most commonly on peat, muck, and sandy soils high in pH, but may be found on any soil type if the pH is too high. A foliar spray of 10 pounds manganese sulfate in 20 gallons of water per acre is effective. The spray should thoroughly wet the leaves when the plants are 6 to 10 inches tall. Manganese may be applied in mixed fertilizer at planting time at about 2½ times the rate suggested for foliar spray. The acidity in the fertilizer helps to keep the manganese in available form in high pH soil. Broadcast application is ineffective.

Molybdenum deficiency. Soils are rarely low in molybdenum. However, the availability of this nutrient to the soybean plant is often very low in strongly acid soils. Plants suffering from a mild deficiency probably will not appear to be greatly different from normal plants, except that they are smaller. Under severe conditions, deficient plants may be so poorly nodulated that they will be pale green, indicating nitrogen deficiency. Molybdenum may be applied as a seed treatment, but little can be done for a growing crop showing signs of this deficiency. Future crops can be protected by applying limestone to increase soil pH.

Nitrogen deficiency. Deficiency of this element is seldom observed, except in fields with no previous history of soybeans and where the planting seed was not inoculated, or where molybdenum is very deficient. Young non-nodulated plants may have pale green or yellowish leaves. Occasionally, nitrogen deficiency symptoms are caused by the soybean cyst nematode, Fusarium rot, or molybdenum deficiency, all of which interfere with nodule development.

Calcium deficiency. The result of this deficiency is poor nodulation, so soybeans growing on calcium-deficient soils exhibit nitrogen deficiency symptoms. Actual calcium deficiency symptoms are seldom observed in soybeans. In 1969, USDA researchers reported a peculiar petiole collapse that was traced to calcium shortage caused by high aluminum content in strongly acid soil.

Manganese toxicity. On acid soils containing abundant iron-manganese pebbles there may be sufficient free manganese to be toxic to soybeans. The plants have crinkled leaves with downward-cupped leaf margins. The youngest leaves on the plant are affected first, therefore, the symptoms appear near the top of the plant. Yellowing between the leaf veins may or may not be observed. Acid soil favors this condition, therefore a limestone application should be made to correct the acidity of the soil.

Phosphorus deficiency. While phosphorus is essential for good soybean growth, there are no clear-cut deficiency symptoms, except that the plants are stunted and the leaves are blue-green. Phosphorus should be applied in the quantity called for by soil test.

Zinc deficiency. Plants suffering from this deficiency have stems and leaves that fail to reach normal size. Some of the tissues between leaf veins turn yellow, a condition which is usually worst on the lowest leaves. The yellowed leaf tissues may turn brown or gray and

49

49. Both seedlings have thickened hypocotyls, but the one on the left has a normal root system. It shows evidence of crust damage. The right-hand seedling is damaged by trifluralin.

50. Atrazine damage

50

51

51. Leaves taken 50, 60, and 80 feet from the edge of a field show progressively decreasing 2,4-D drift damage.

die prematurely. This deficiency occurs in the presence of high phosphorus and high pH with free lime. For soil treatment, zinc sulfate is the most widely used material. The suggested rate is 10 pounds of actual zinc (30 pounds zinc sulfate) per acre on silt and clay soils, 3 to 5 pounds on sands. The zinc should be broadcast and worked in, or placed in a band at least two inches to the side and two inches below the seed. Foliar applications are detailed on page 86.

Boron toxicity. Soybeans are extremely sensitive to boron, which stunts affected plants. The older leaves fall off in extreme cases. The leaves are crinkled, with the edges cupped either up or down. Dying begins at the leaf margins without any previous yellowing, followed by spreading of dead areas over the entire leaf. This deficiency is favored by heavy boron application, especially near the row and on sandy soils. Boron should not be used for soybeans.

Miscellaneous Soybean Troubles

Herbicide damage. The margin of safety is relatively narrow with most soybean herbicides. Many cases of crop damage can be traced to mistakes in application. However, even excessive rainfall following planting and application of a pre-emergence herbicide may result in damage. Fortunately, the soybean plant usually outgrows herbicide injury with little or no effect on yield. Only occasionally is there some loss of stand.

Normally, herbicide injury that warrants concern can be distinguished from other problems, such as disease. Minor injury, on the other hand, may be difficult to identify.

A grower who suspects herbicide damage should examine the plant root as well as the tops. The root system often holds the key to identification. If the roots are deformed, the problem is likely to be herbicide injury. Some growth abnormalities associated with injury by herbicides cleared for use on soybeans are as follows:

1. Stunted plants with stunted, proliferated root systems (amiben).
2. Stunted plants with roots growing upward instead of downward (alanap).
3. Stunted plants with thickened hypocotyls and limited, but thickened and stubby roots (trifluralin).

Note: The thickened hypocotyl also is caused when a crust or compacted soil interferes with seedling emergence. However, plants in these latter cases have normal, healthy root systems.

4. Stunted plants similar to those in the preceding description, except with some leaves smaller than normal and crinkled (vernolate).

Soybeans may be injured by residues of herbicides applied to preceding crops, such as corn or cotton. The injury symptoms vary, but characteristically the soybean seedlings emerge and appear perfectly normal for a while. Then, as their root systems grow and more residual herbicide is taken up, the leaves become discolored and develop dead margins or spots. The affected plants may outgrow the damage or die, depending on the amount of residue present.

When the herbicide has been applied to the preceding crop in bands, there may be a definite pattern of damage in the soybean field. Soybean plants growing along the margins of the previous year's bands may be less severely damaged than those in the center of the bands. Perfectly normal leaves will appear at the tops of plants that outgrow the injury. Residual damage from atrazine typifies this type of injury. Precautions for avoiding this type of damage are spelled out on labels of herbicides that carry residual danger.

Soybeans may be damaged by drifting spray or vapor of some herbicides. Because of the widespread use of 2,4-D and 2,4,5-T in fencerows and along roadsides, drift damage of these chemicals probably is more common than that of other herbicides. The type of injury symptom will vary with the herbicide. Drift damage usually can be distinguished from disease by the pattern of damage in the affected field. All plants in the affected area will exhibit the same symptoms. However, drift damage is usually most severe around the edges of a field. Weeds can help identify the problem; if they show similar damage, herbicide drift is probably the cause.

Lightning. This damage is sometimes mistaken for a parasitic disease. But it is easily distinguished from disease damage by the sudden death of the plants in the affected area and the fact that both soybeans and weeds are killed. Additionally, the affected area, usually circular-shaped, does not increase in size. The area may be as large as 50 feet in diameter.

Crusting. A hard crust may form when beating rain falls on fine-textured soil. The germinating soybean is sometimes unable to break such a crust. When this is the case, the seedlings may completely deplete the food stored in their cotyledons before they emerge. The stems of these seedlings are characteristically thickened. This thickening may also occur when the surface soil is compacted by frequent, heavy rain. The most severe damage resulting from a soil crust will be the actual breaking of the hypocotyl arch. Rotary hoeing to break the crust may help emergence.

Frost. Late spring frosts sometimes damage soybeans in the northern production area. Frost-damaged plants should be carefully examined. If all above-

53

53. Hail damage

ground tissue is damaged, the soybean should be replanted. Quite often, only the upper part of the plant is damaged and the regrowth promptly appears at one of the undamaged nodes. When the extent of damage is difficult to estimate, a grower should replant between the existing rows. If the regrowth comes on strong and vigorous, and the number of severely damaged plants is small, the replant may be cultivated out. On the other hand, if the replant appears to be the better bet, it can be left and the damaged rows cultivated out.

Water Damage. Soybeans yield best on well-drained soils, and will die if submerged for long. The length of time that they can survive complete submergence depends on whether the water is still or moving, and the temperature. If not submerged, soybeans can stand flooding relatively well.

In a University of Arkansas flood irrigation experiment, researchers studied the effect of leaving water on the soybean field for longer than the usual two days at first irrigation. Flooding occurred at first bloom stage. Dorman and Lee varieties were used. Lee appeared to be more flood-tolerant than Dorman. Neither variety was adversely affected unless the irrigation water was permitted to stand for more than seven days. In one case the yield of Lee, flooded for 21 days, equalled that of Lee flooded only two days. The occurrence of temperatures greater than 90 degrees appeared to cause severe yield reduction when the flooding lasted longer than seven days.

The death of soybeans in low areas may be caused by phytophthora rot instead of water damage. This disease, however, is favored by poor drainage and wet soil. It is such a problem in some areas that a phytophthora-resistant variety is the first prerequisite to success with irrigation.

Hail. This type of damage is easily recognized. Leaves are severely slashed, with large areas of tissue missing. The decision of whether to replant or keep the original stand may be arrived at in the same way as that suggested for frost damage.

Is replanting desirable?

The decision to tear up a poor stand and replant is made relatively easily if the stand is a near-failure and the normal planting season has not ended. The decision becomes more difficult as the season advances. Some factors to be considered are:
a. The danger of a killing frost catching the replant before maturity.
b. The probable yield of the existing stand versus the probable yield of a good stand planted late.
c. Increased crop costs.
d. The increased risk of having an overly dry seedbed.
e. The possible need to remove weeds by tillage before replanting.
f. The high harvest losses that result from low podding and branching on widely spaced plants in a poor stand.

8

Harvesting, Storage and Marketing

Harvest is one of the most critical steps in profitable soybean production. It takes about 30 bushels per acre to pay the cost of producing a 40-bushel crop. That leaves 10 bushels as potential profit. If a 10 percent harvesting loss (four bushels) occurs, the profit is reduced by 40 percent. Some agricultural engineers say that the average soybean grower loses at least this much of his crop.

A well-adjusted machine helps keep harvesting losses low. Choice of variety, row width, plant population, and topography of the field are a few other factors that influence losses. Most soybeans left in the field during harvest never get inside the combine. Preharvest shatter and gathering failures account for 80 to 85 percent of all harvesting losses.

Preharvest Losses

Preharvest shatter is influenced by variety, weather, and timeliness of harvest. The best way to hold shattering losses to a minimum is to plant shatter-resistant varieties. In comparison plots, Harosoy 63 soybeans reached a moisture content of 13 percent on September 28. Preharvest shattering was very low, but after 10 days of wet weather in early October, the soybeans began to shatter. Within a week, losses were as high as 20 percent. Meanwhile, the shatter loss in Shelby, a shatter-resistant variety, was negligible under the same conditions.

Unfortunately, shatter-resistant varieties are not available for all locations and conditions. The next

1. **Harvest management is an important part of turning high-yielding soybeans into profit. The crop and the field must be in proper condition, the combine must be well-adjusted, and the operator must be careful.**

151

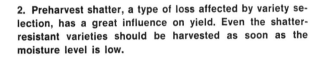

2. Preharvest shatter, a type of loss affected by variety selection, has a great influence on yield. Even the shatter-resistant varieties should be harvested as soon as the moisture level is low.

3. Soybeans are sampled and graded thoroughly. If they have been harvested carelessly and contain splits, foreign matter, or excess moisture, they will be discounted.

best preventive step is to start harvesting as soon as the moisture is low enough. It is particularly important to start early because the moisture content of soybeans declines rapidly when the humidity is low. In one case, Shelby soybeans declined from 42 percent moisture on September 9 to 13 percent on September 14, for a loss of 29 percent in five days.

Soybeans should contain less than 13 percent moisture at harvest if they are to be stored without the benefit of artificial drying. The maximum allowable moisture content of the No. 1 market grade is 13 percent. However, soybeans can be combined at moisture levels somewhat greater than this without damage in the combine. Therefore, the moisture content at which harvesting begins depends on the market and availability of drying facilities. Discounts for excessive moisture or the costs of drying may make the harvest of high moisture beans uneconomical.

If soybeans are being harvested for use as planting seed, particular attention should be given to proper combine adjustment. The soybean seedcoat is easily cracked or damaged during the harvesting process.

Water and detrimental organisms readily enter through the breaks in the seedcoat and germination is reduced.

Gathering Losses

Choice of variety is a factor in holding gathering losses to a minimum. Beans left on the stubble or on uncut or lodged stalks may add up to heavy gathering losses. Both the height of the first pod above the ground and susceptibility to lodging are varietal characteristics.

The height at which the cutterbar is operated also affects gathering losses. A cutterbar set too high will miss the lowest pods. Cutting high also contributes to shatter losses because most of the beans in cut pods will drop to the ground.

The cutterbar should be run just as close to the ground as possible. The combine operator can watch the field conditions and raise and lower the header as the field profile varies. This requires careful and constant attention. Many growers install automatic header control devices that regulate the height of the cutterbar. These attachments work best under dry soil conditions. When the soil is dry and the combine well adjusted, they aid in keeping gathering losses to a minimum. In Ohio State University tests, gathering losses have been held to as low as .7 bushel per acre by the use of an automatic header control in weed-free beans, when other conditions, such as moisture, were favorable.

4. The height at which the combine cutterbar is operated can have a great effect on harvest loss. Some varieties set pods higher than others and are therefore easier to combine, but cultural practices also affect podding height.

Effect of cutting height on yield

Height of cut	Yield (bushels per acre)	Loss (bushels per acre)	Loss (percent)
Hand harvested	33.6	0	0
3.5 inches	31.8	1.8	5.4
5.0 inches	30.5	3.2	9.4
6.5 inches	29.5	4.1	12.2

Iowa State University

4

5. Plant spacing in the row changes podding height. This variety normally sets its lowest pods well above the soil line, but here, with the plants six inches apart, the lowest pods are too close to the ground to be combined.

5

Reel Speed Important

Ohio State University engineers have identified excessive reel speed in relation to ground speed as a major reason for shatter loss at the cutter bar. When properly set, the reel has a peripheral speed about 25 percent greater than the ground speed.

The reel speed can be determined by the following procedure: Measure the circumference of the reel. Then drive 100 feet at the ground speed to be used in the field. Count the number of reel revolutions. If the reel has a circumference of 12.5 feet, it should make 10 revolutions (125 feet) while the combine travels the 100 feet. The correct speed can be attained by varying either the speed of the reel or the ground speed of the combine. If the combine does not have a variable reel speed, the only way of obtaining the correct reel speed in relation to ground speed is by regulating the ground speed.

The crop condition and height dictate the position of the reel (its exact location in relation to the cutter bar also varies with the type of reel). Normally, the reel is set so its axis is further ahead of the cutter bar for lodged soybeans than those standing erect. This is particularly true of the pickup-type reel, in which case the bats or tines pass closer to the cutter bar in lodged soybeans than in standing beans. The reel should be set so it is just deep enough in the crop to move the beans over the cutter bar. The bats or tines should leave the beans just after they are cut.

The ground speed of the combine should be ad-

justed to the crop condition. In a University of Illinois test the harvest losses were greater at two mph in weedy soybeans than at four mph in clean soybeans. Gathering losses tend to increase as ground speed increases. More pods are left on the stubble and more shattering occurs at high speed because the cutter bar tends to run higher off the ground. There is also an increase in the number of pods stripped from the plant at speeds above three mph. In addition, threshing and separating losses increase with speed in weedy soybeans.

Soybeans are rubbed out of the pod easily and their size and shape make them easy to clean. Norm-

7

6

6. Pods left on the stubble can add up to heavy losses. An automatic header control device can help keep the cutterbar as low as possible, minimizing such losses.

8

7. The beans in pods on cut stalks are classified as stalk loss. They are part of the total harvesting loss.

8. Lodged plants may be missed completely by the combine cutterbar. Lodging loss is a severe problem with some varieties, and under certain environmental conditions.

Rectangular dimensions for 10-square-foot plot

Machine swath (feet)	Distance in inches to cover 10 square feet
8	15
10	12
12	10
13	9.25
14	8.6
16	7.5
18	6.6
20	6.0

For combines with swath widths greater than 20 feet, the operator should measure off a 20-square-foot area and divide the number of beans on the ground by 80, instead of 40 as directed in the instructions below. This will avoid the use of rectangular measuring areas less than 6 inches wide. In all cases, it is important to span the entire combine swath with the measuring rectangle. For a 22-foot swath the rectangle should be 10.9 inches wide; for a 24-foot swath, 10 inches wide.

ally the recommendations for cylinder speed and other machine adjustments given in the combine operator's manual will give excellent machine results.

Low humidity complicates harvesting. Shatter losses and cracking increase when the moisture content drops below 13 percent. These losses will be at a minimum early in the morning when the pods and stalks are damp with dew, or soon after a light rainfall. However, to harvest under these conditions requires an increase over regular cylinder speed. It is therefore to the grower's advantage to use a combine having a variable speed cylinder. This will permit the cylinder speed to be decreased gradually during the day as the moisture leaves the plants.

Measuring Harvest Losses

D. M. Byg, agricultural engineer at Ohio State University, has the following to say about determining harvest loss: "The method of loss measurement that I have found most practical is based upon the number of beans lost per unit area. An average of four beans per square foot represents a loss of approximately one bushel per acre. In order to make bean counts easy and fast, tie a string to four wire stakes or pins such that the rectangle enclosed by this string is equal to the machine swath and the length is great enough to enclose 10 square feet. The table above lists rectangular dimensions for various machine widths.

"To determine total crop loss, stop the combine well in from edges of the field and where beans are

9. Throwing excessive amounts of soil into the row at the time these soybeans were cultivated may have improved weed control, but it will complicate harvest. The combine operator will be unable to run the cutterbar low enough to harvest the lowest pods.

9

10

10. The combine reel causes serious shatter loss if operated too fast. The peripheral speed of the reel should be about 25 percent greater than the combine ground speed.

155

11   Moisture content affects harvest loss

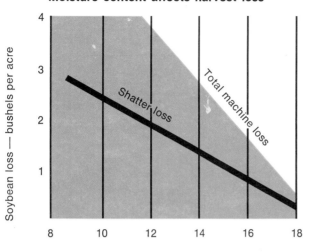

11. As crop moisture content declines, harvest loss and preharvest losses increase.

13-14. Checking harvest losses and making machine adjustments is a vitally important part of combining soybeans efficiently. The first step to identification of gathering unit losses is to reverse the combine for about 20 feet and span the swath with a measuring frame (14) of appropriate dimensions. All beans are counted (13).

13   1

representative of the entire crop," Byg continues. "Place rectangular frame across machine swath just harvested and count all beans in this area. Divide by 40 and you have the total loss in bushels per acre. If this loss is in the neighborhood of three to five percent of your yield, it is within allowable limits; if it is three to five bushels per acre, then you should pinpoint the source of loss.

"To determine preharvest loss, place rectangular frame in standing beans ahead of the combine. Count all beans on the ground, free from stalks. Divide by 40 to get the preharvest loss in bushels per acre. Subtract this loss from the total loss to get the machine loss.

"To determine gathering unit loss, stop the forward movement of the combine and quickly disengage the

clutch of the gathering unit. Then back up the combine about 20 feet. Place the rectangular frame across the machine swath in front of the combine. Count all beans found in this area and subtract the preharvest loss count. Divide the remainder by 40 and you have the gathering unit loss in bushels per acre. When making this bean count, you can pinpoint the source of gathering unit loss by first counting: (a) the shatter loss (loose beans and pods free of stalk); (b) the stubble loss (beans in pods on stubble); (c) the lodged loss (beans in pods on uncut stalks); (d) the stalk loss (beans in pods on cut stalks). Divide each of the above counts by 40 to get bushels per acre.

"To calculate cylinder and separation loss, subtract the gathering unit loss from the machine loss. It is not feasible to differentiate between the cylinder and separation losses by the kernel count method."

Storage

Molds and insects are the primary causes of quality deterioration in stored grain. Both are favored by high moisture and warm temperatures, as well as the presence of damaged grain and excessive foreign material in the soybeans.

Moisture, the key to successful storage, is more critical for soybeans than some other crops. The moisture content of soybeans should be about one percent less than that of corn under identical storage conditions. In order to protect germination quality, seed soybeans should be stored at one percent less

12

Expected loss at 30 bushel yield level

Loss source	Average harvesting job	Excellent harvesting job
Shatter	1.8	0.7
Stubble	0.6	0.3
Lodged and stalk	1.0	0.4
Cylinder	0.2	Nil
Separation	0.2	0.1
Total loss (bushels per acre)	3.8	1.5

16. Soybeans placed in unaerated storage during the fall lose heat slowly as the outside temperature declines. Beans near the surface and next to the walls cool first. Cool air moves down the inside walls, forcing warm air upward. When the warm air reaches the cool surface, condensation occurs. This process may continue as long as there is a temperature differential in the soybeans. Aeration prevents all this by cooling the interior mass.

15. Storing soybeans on the farm for deferred sale is a way of increasing crop returns in some years.

Moisture migration in a grain bin

16

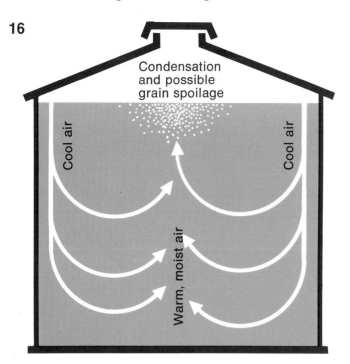

Condensation and possible grain spoilage

Cool air

Cool air

Warm, moist air

Horsepower requirements for aerating soybeans

Grain depth (feet) Airflow (cubic feet per minute per bushel)	Up to 20		20 to 30		30 to 40		40 to 50	
	1/10	1/30	1/10	1/30	1/10	1/30	1/10	1/30
Bushels	Horsepower							
2,000	1/20	1/50	1/12	1/50	1/6	1/50	1/6	1/50
3,000	1/12	1/50	1/6	1/20	1/6	1/20	1/4	1/20
6,000	1/6	1/20	1/4	1/20	1/3	1/20	1/2	1/12
10,000	1/4	1/12	1/3	1/12	1/2	1/12	3/4	1/6
20,000	1/2	1/6	3/4	1/6	1	1/6	1½	1/4
30,000	3/4	3/4	1	1/4	1½	1/4	2	1/3
40,000	1	1/3	1½	1/3	2	1/3	3	1/2
60,000	1½	1/2	2	1/2	3	1/2	5	3/4

moisture than those to be sold for processing.

Temperature, also important, is related to moisture content. Wet soybeans may be stored much longer at 35 degrees than at 75 degrees. Therefore, the moisture content that is considered safe for storing soybeans in the northern production region will be too high for safe storage in the South.

■ In the central Corn Belt, soybeans containing up to 14 percent moisture usually may be stored safely from harvest until late winter. But this moisture content is too high for safe storage during spring and summer. If the storage period is expected to run into spring and summer, the moisture content should be no higher, and preferably lower than 13 percent.

■ In the southern production region, the moisture content should be lower. The Georgia Experiment Station suggests 11 percent as the maximum moisture content for long-term storage in the northern part of the state; 10 percent as the maximum in southern Georgia.

Aeration of stored soybeans is usually required because temperature differences within the stored beans cause an undesirable migration of moisture. This is triggered by the fact that newly harvested and stored soybeans are warmer than the outside air.

As the outside temperatures decline in late fall and winter, the soybeans near the surface and outside walls of a storage bin cool. Those soybeans in the interior of the mass, however, remain warm. The difference in temperature causes a circulation of air

from the cool soybeans down the walls and then upward into the warm soybeans. As the cool air moves upward, it is first warmed, then cooled again as it reaches the surface of the grain.

As the air is warmed during its upward movement, it picks up moisture. Then, because cool air holds less moisture than warm air, the air releases moisture, causing condensation on the cool surface layer of soybeans. This layer may become quite high in moisture, providing an ideal place for mold to grow when temperatures are favorable.

Aeration prevents condensation because it cools the interior mass of soybeans. A motor-driven fan and air duct or perforated floor in the storage facility are needed for aeration. Plans and information concerning duct size and air distribution systems are available from agricultural experiment stations and dealers of grain storage structures.

The cost of aerating grain is relatively small. Horsepower requirements to aerate soybeans are given above.

Artificial Drying

Soybeans combined at 14 percent moisture or more should be dried if they are being placed in storage.

The maximum drying temperature for soybeans is the same as that for corn — about 130 to 140 degrees, unless the soybeans are to be used for seed. In this case, the temperature should not exceed 110 degrees. In drying soybeans, a grower is seldom confronted

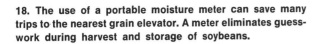

18. The use of a portable moisture meter can save many trips to the nearest grain elevator. A meter eliminates guesswork during harvest and storage of soybeans.

 18

19. Jimsonweed and other broadleaf weeds present combining problems and add to soybean harvest losses.

Quick reference to shrinkage losses

Initial moisture content (percent)	Percent shrinkage at seven moisture levels to which soybeans are dried						
	13.0	13.5	14.0	14.5	15.0	15.5	16.0
13.5	.58						
14.0	1.15	.58					
14.5	1.73	1.15	.58				
15.0	2.30	1.73	1.16	.58			
15.5	2.87	2.31	1.74	1.17	.59		
16.0	3.45	2.89	2.33	1.75	1.18	.59	
16.5	4.02	3.47	2.91	2.34	1.77	1.18	.60
17.0	4.60	4.05	3.49	2.92	2.35	1.78	1.20
17.5	5.17	4.62	4.07	3.51	2.94	2.37	1.79
18.0	5.77	5.20	4.65	4.09	3.53	2.96	2.38
18.5	6.32	5.78	5.23	4.68	4.12	3.55	2.98
19.0	6.90	6.36	5.81	5.26	4.71	4.14	3.58
19.5	7.47	6.94	6.40	5.85	5.29	4.73	4.17
20.0	8.05	7.51	6.98	6.43	5.88	5.33	4.77

with removing more than two or three points of moisture. A boost of 20 degrees over the temperature of the outside air is usually adequate.

Since there is a danger of cracking soybeans, they should be handled as little as possible after drying. It is also wise to remove only enough moisture to make the soybeans storable.

A grower who dries his soybeans should own a moisture tester. It will save the time and expense of taking samples to the elevator, and can help prevent overdrying. If soybeans are overdried by two percent (to a level of 11 percent), the grower loses more than 2.25 out of every 100 bushels.

Defoliation to Hasten Harvest

Research results show that soybean yields are reduced when the leaves are removed before the time of natural loss. At Stoneville, Mississippi, soybeans defoliated three weeks before normal maturity were ready for combining only three days earlier than those that matured normally. The defoliated soybeans produced 30 percent less than those maturing normally. At Urbana, Illinois, defoliation anytime prior to 50 percent normal leaf drop is accompanied by a reduction in yield. Obviously, there is no advantage to be gained from defoliating at that late date.

Desiccation of Green Weeds

The presence of weeds is a problem at soybean harvest time. This is especially true if the weeds re-

Soybean production, use and carryover

21

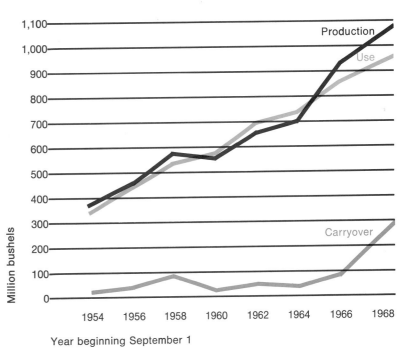

The yield of soy oil and meal

20

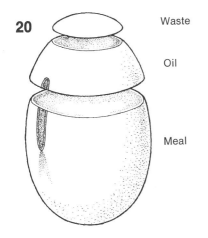

Waste

Oil

Meal

main green and succulent after the crop is mature and ready for harvest. Research at the Delta Branch Experiment Station showed that combine losses equalled five bushels per acre when soybeans were infested with pigweed or cocklebur at the rate of one weed per six square feet. A question has been raised about the use of chemicals to kill and dry the green weeds in ripe soybeans. When this book went to press, no chemical desiccant was approved for use on soybeans intended for food, feed, or oil.

Marketing

For the first time in the history of soybean production in the United States, a burdensome carryover existed at the end of the 1968 season. This means that the price trends and patterns established over a long period of simultaneously expanding production and demand may not apply in the future.

A bushel of processed soybeans yields about 11 pounds of oil and 48 pounds of meal. During the 1958-67 period, the average value of the oil from a bushel of soybeans was $1.06, and that of the meal, $1.62. In other words, the oil accounted for about 40 percent of the total value, the meal about 60 percent. During the same 10-year period the average price received by farmers was $2.36 per bushel. This means the per-bushel value of soy products included 32 cents for handling and crushing ($2.68 — $2.36 = $0.32.)

The 10-year average price paid to farmers in the

20. A bushel of soybeans yields about 11 pounds of oil and 48 pounds of meal. The balance is processing loss. The actual yields of oil and meal vary by years and locations. Cool August temperatures lower oil content; high temperatures increase it.

21. Curves indicating the production, use and carryover of soybeans reveal dramatic growth in the industry over a 14-year period, and point to a bulging carryover.

United States shows a fairly consistent pattern. The price usually is lowest in October, at harvest time. It gradually increases to a peak in April of the following year. It declines slightly from this high until August and then drops again to the season low during harvest.

There are exceptions to the normal trend. In only four years out of 11 did the price actually peak in April. Three times it peaked in May, and once in November. These exceptions make the study of the market exciting and often quite profitable for growers who store and hold their soybeans.

The soybean has many competitors in the market. The price of oil is influenced by the world supply of and demand for at least 20 other fats and oils. The price of meal is more directly tied to domestic livestock numbers and demand. However, the export of both soybean meal and unprocessed soybeans has become an increasingly important price influence over the past 15 years.

In livestock feeding, soybean protein has already

22

Average price per bushel paid farmers for soybeans, by months, 1958-69

	Sept.	Oct.	Nov.	Dec.	Jan.	Feb.	Mar.	Apr.	May	June	July	Aug.
1958-59	1.98	1.93	1.89	1.97	2.02	2.05	2.07	2.10	2.13	2.09	2.05	1.98
1959-60	1.90	1.93	2.00	1.98	2.01	1.99	1.99	2.02	2.00	1.97	1.97	1.99
1960-61	1.97	1.94	1.96	1.99	2.23	2.48	2.68	3.02	2.96	2.60	2.48	2.49
1961-62	2.24	2.20	2.27	2.30	2.32	2.32	2.34	2.38	2.36	2.34	2.35	2.33
1962-63	2.25	2.23	2.30	2.35	2.41	2.50	2.51	2.45	2.47	2.48	2.44	2.45
1963-64	2.44	2.56	2.66	2.58	2.65	2.57	2.55	2.45	2.36	2.35	2.34	2.35
1964-65	2.51	2.55	2.57	2.71	2.73	2.81	2.85	2.85	2.72	2.74	2.69	2.53
1965-66	2.35	2.31	2.36	2.48	2.67	2.77	2.71	2.78	2.90	3.04	3.37	3.49
1966-67	2.97	2.78	2.80	2.82	2.77	2.71	2.74	2.71	2.69	2.71	2.66	2.56
1967-68	2.53	2.44	2.43	2.48	2.53	2.57	2.57	2.56	2.58	2.54	2.52	2.51
1968-69	2.40	2.32	2.40	2.42	2.46	2.48	2.48	2.51	2.56	2.52	2.52	2.51
Average	2.32	2.29	2.33	2.37	2.44	2.48	2.50	2.53	2.52	2.49	2.49	2.47

■ Expected peak   ■ Mildly unusual peak   ■ Abnormal peak

22. Soybean prices are expected to peak in April. In only four years during the last 11, however, did they do so, as indicated by the green blocks. Blue blocks are mildly unusual peaks; red blocks, abnormal peaks.

met serious competition from urea. It will meet even more competition in the future. Three possibilities include: 1) Other high protein crops. Plant breeders can genetically manipulate both the quantity and the quality of protein in crops, such as corn. High lysine corn is an example. 2) Synthetic amino acids. Some of these building blocks of protein can be produced synthetically on a large scale. 3) Petroleum-origin protein. Microbiological cultures can be grown on petroleum sources to produce protein for feed.

When conditions of supply and price are the same as the preceeding year, it is best to hold for a price rise. In 1966, Dr. T. A. Hieronymus of the University of Illinois set forth these general rules concerning soybean prices:

—The price of a comparatively short crop usually peaks early.

—The price of oil is sensitive to the world supply and demand situation and tends to move in long cycles. All other things being equal, the price of soybeans moves in the direction of oil prices.

—The price of meal is sensitive to changes in livestock numbers, particularly hogs. Growers should hold soybeans when an increase in the spring pig crop is anticipated.

—Meal consumption is responsive to price. A high price for meal in the fall and winter often results in a decreasing price in the spring and summer, and vice versa.

—The price of soybeans is responsive to general inflation-deflation conditions and moves in general sympathy with the prices of other commodities. It is also very sensitive to news of international unrest.

—Speculative activity in both cash and futures by farmers and others is very important in determining the seasonal pattern of soybean prices. There is a tendency to put the price either too high or too low at harvest and a tendency to remember only last year. This yields an every-other-year flavor to soybean holding. Thus the most profitable procedure might well be to do what would have been unprofitable the year before.

It should be pointed out that these rules were developed when both production and demand were increasing and there was no appreciable supply at the end of the season. Their accuracy for the future is yet to be confirmed.

23. In world oil markets the soybean has many competitors, including sunflower oil, palm oil, fish oil, corn oil, and butterfat. Soybean meal faces competition also.

9

Every portion
of this elegant
dinner is
enhanced by
soy protein.

Soybeans: Food, Feed and Future

The soybean is a remarkable plant. It is an antique — one of the oldest of all food plants — and a modern-day success with many uses. It is a highly efficient producer of protein and oil, both of which are very well adapted to the nourishment of animal or man.

The soybean as a human food has helped shape the history of the world. Most authors credit the earliest writings on soybeans to Emperor Shennung who is said to have ruled in China in 2838 B.C. The study of the antiquity of the crop has recently been renewed and there is some question concerning this statement. Nevertheless, soybeans have been used for human food in China since long before the birth of Christ. More recently, the soybean has become the most important source of edible oil in the western world.

By the start of World War II, German chemists and nutritionists had developed a soy oil product that could replace lard at 50 percent of the cost. They had worked out recipes using the soybean in the German diet as a substitute for meat protein. And the soybean was the basis of an antifatigue biscuit for soldiers on the march. *The London Times* said in mid-1940, "The soya has become vitally important to Germany from the food, the economic, and the military standpoint."

Low-Cost Protein Foods

Soybean products are important in the formulation of new, low-cost, nutritionally balanced protein foods and drinks manufactured and distributed in several protein-deficient countries. The impact of these on

CSM ingredients

	percent
Corn meal (processed)	64
Soy flour (toasted)	24
Nonfat dry milk	5
Minerals, vitamins	2
Soy oil	5

1. In three years USDA shipped more than one billion pounds of corn-soya-milk mix to 61 foreign countries. The blend is cooked with water in preparing a gruel.

the future welfare of those nations is yet to be observed. (Soy milk has been used for centuries in the Orient.)

The newest drinks are cheaply formulated, usually with at least three percent protein. They are sold as powders to be mixed with water or as bottled liquids. They are developed to please the palate of the people in the country where they are sold. Hopefully, they will become popular and thereby contribute to improving the diet of many nations.

The new protein foods are the result of newly developed blends with other grains and new processing methods. The blended foods are commonly referred

2. Soy protein is processed in many forms for food use. The spun soy protein fibers (top) are colored and flavored to simulate meat and used to fortify and extend low-cost red meat, poultry, and seafood. Some products made from the fibers are (clockwise) meat-like nuggets, ham-type cubes, poultry meat extender, red meat extender, ground beef type granules, bacon-like chips, and (center) chicken-like cubes.

to as CSM and WSB. CSM — corn-soy-milk mix — is a blend of processed cornmeal, toasted soybean flour and nonfat dry milk. A vitamin-mineral mixture is also incorporated in the blend. CSM can be prepared as a gruel if cooked in water for one or two minutes. The short cooking time is important because of the shortage of fuel in some countries.

WSB — wheat-soy blend — has a minimum protein content of 20 percent and oil content of 6 percent, as does CSM. WSB is made either with regular wheat flour or bulgur flour blended with wheat concentrate. This flour is mixed with soy flour and soy oil. It is also supplemented with essential minerals and vitamins.

Large quantities of CSM and WSB have been shipped by the United States government to food- and protein-deficient countries.

New methods of processing soy flour make possible high-protein products that can be colored, flavored, and shaped almost at will. An example is the synthetic meats which are flavored and structured to look like chicken, turkey, ham, bacon, and beef. The production of these is relatively expensive. Less expensive products ranging from 50 to 65 percent protein are being marketed in several protein-deficient countries.

A major obstacle in supplementing the protein or food supply of a country has been that of pleasing the local palate. These new high-protein products which can be flavored and structured into various shapes afford a new opportunity to do this.

Over 90 percent of the soybean oil produced finds its way into the human diet. A little over half is used in margarine and shortening.

Well over 90 percent of the soybean meal is used in feeding livestock. However, the portion used in human food has continued to increase since 1929 when the first edible soy flour and soy grits were produced commercially. For human food uses, soy protein products fall in three distinct categories:

— Soy flours and grits contain 40 to 60 percent protein. These materials are similar, but grits are coarser than the flours. Oil may be added to flours for special food uses. At 7 cents per pound the average soy flour or grits (50 percent protein) supply protein for 14 cents a pound.

— Soy protein concentrate has at least 70 percent protein. It can be manufactured in a variety of particle sizes. At 20 cents per pound, the 70 percent concentrate supplies protein for 29 cents a pound.

— Isolated soy protein contains 90 to 97 percent protein, and is obviously the most highly concentrated form of soy protein. It is a spray-dried product. The 90 percent material, at 35 cents a pound, provides protein for about 39 cents a pound.

The flour and grits, the lowest priced materials, contain fiber and sugar which detract from desired flavors. The concentrate has no soluble sugar, and can therefore, be given artificial flavors. It is used in calf milk replacers. The isolate contains only selected proteins, can accept flavorings, and may have a gelling characteristic.

Soybeans

Defatted Flake Products

Soy flour and grits

Edible Uses

Industrial Uses
Adhesive
Plywood
Wallboard
Insecticidal sprays
Particle board
Tape joint cements
Linoleum backing
Texture paints
Nutrient
Yeast
Antibiotic
Beer & ale

Edible Uses
Bakery Ingredient
Bread
Baked goods
Cookies
Crackers
Doughnuts
Alimentary Pastes
Noodles
Meat Products
Specialty sausage
Meat patties
Chili con carne
Cereals
Ready-to-eat
Canned
Hot-type
Prepared Mixes
Pancake & waffle
Cake Mixes
Food Drinks
900-calorie type
Beverage powders
Baby Food
Dry concentrates
Canned
Hypo-allergenic milk
Confections
Candy products
Special Diet Foods
Diabetic
Allergenic
High protein
Textured Vegetable Protein
Simulated meat, fruit, nut products

Soy protein concentrate
Bakery ingredient
Meat additive

Soybean meal

Feed Uses
Livestock Feeds
Poultry Feeds
Protein Concentrates
Pet Foods

Industrial Uses
Fertilizer
Carrier
Vitamins
Antibiotics
Drugs

Isolated soy protein

Edible Uses
Food Additive
To increase protein content and improve nutritive value
Simulated Meat Products
Spun fibers for imitation meats
Dehydrated meat bits
Aerating Agent
Chiffon pies
Marshmallow
Frappes & fondants
Beverages
Soy Milk
Food drinks
Infant formulations
Dietary items

Industrial Uses
Adhesive
Paper coating
Water emulsion paints
Sizing
Textile
Paper
Fiber
Vegetable wool
Fiber bristles

Mill Feed

High Fiber Feeds
Carrier
Vitamin
Antibiotics
Drugs

Natural Full Fat Products

Soybean Products

Baked Soybeans
Seed
Soybean Sprouts
Stock Feeds

Full Fat Soy Flour
Bread
Candy
Doughnut Mix
Frozen Desserts
Pancake Flour
Pan Grease Extender
Pie Crust
Sweet Goods
Low-Cost Gruels
Infant Milk Drinks

Roasted Soybeans
Candy Ingredient
Confection
Cookie Ingredient
Cookie Topping
Cracker Ingredient
Fountain Topping
Soy Coffee
Soynut Butter
Spice Base
Dietary Items

Soybean Derivatives
Oriental Foods

Oil Products

Crude Soybean Oil

Sterols
Stigmasterol
Sitosterol
Tocopherol
Hormones

Fatty acids

Glycerol

Refined soybean oil

Edible Uses
Antibiotic Mfr.
Cooking Oils
Mayonnaise
Margarine
Pharmaceuticals
Salad Dressings
Salad Oils
Sandwich Spreads
Vegetable Shortening
Mellorine
Medicinals

Technical Uses
Caulking Compounds
Core Oils
Disinfectants
Electrical Insulation
Insecticides
Linoleum Backing
Oiled Fabrics
Printing Inks
Protective Coatings
Plasticizers
Putty
Soap
Waterproof Cement
Wallboard

Soybean lecithin

Edible Uses
Emulsifying Agent
Bakery products
Candy products
Surface Active Agent
Beverage powders
Chocolate coatings
Pharmaceuticals
Nutritional
Medical use
Dietary use
Anti-Spattering Agent
Margarine
Stabilizing Agent
Shortening
Pan Grease

Technical Uses
Anti-Foam Agent
Yeast
Alcohol
Dispersing Agent
Paint
Ink
Insecticides
Rubber
Wetting Agent
Cosmetics
Pigments (paint)
Calf milk replacers
Powdered metals
Textiles
Chemicals
Stabilizing Agent
Emulsions
Mold Release

3

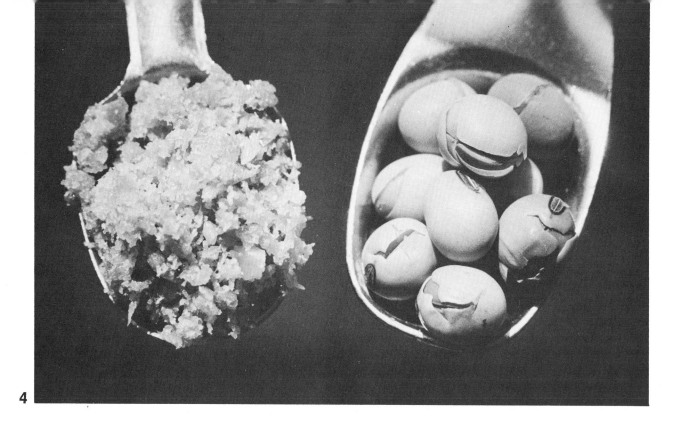

4

5

4. On-farm processing of soybeans for livestock feed opens new opportunities for many growers. Soybeans processed by high-pressure extrusion (left) have a flaky texture and do not require grinding. Dry roasted beans are cracked during processing (right) but must be ground before being used as feed.

5. Livestock feeding consumes more than 90 percent of the soybean meal produced in the United States, although human food uses of soy protein are increasing.

In bakery products, soy flour is used as a bleaching agent and to improve flavor and toasting characteristics. It also extends shelf life by helping retain moisture. In addition, the soy flour improves dough-handling characteristics. This is particularly desirable in making products such as cookies. In doughnuts it reduces the amount of fat absorbed in the frying process, helping to prevent sogginess. In pancakes and waffles a little soy flour reduces the tendency to stick to the griddle. The amount of soy flour in bakery products ranges from less than 1 percent to as great as 15 percent.

Large volumes of soy flour also go into baby foods, low-calorie foods, and dietetic foods. In these uses the high quality of the protein is an asset. Soy flour and soy protein are used in the meat industry to improve the consistency and texture of processed meats.

Relatively new uses for soybean flour or protein isolates include the synthetic meats mentioned previously, synthetic coffee creams, whipped toppings, icings, and other whipped foods requiring a light fluffy structure.

While industry is finding new uses for soy protein in the edible and nonedible areas, the total amount consumed is negligible when compared to the volume used in animal feeding.

The soybean is a major source of lecithins, waxy materials that have many uses. Lecithins are used in emulsifying fats and oils, in assuring good mixing of dry ingredients, and in protecting food flavors by serving as antioxidants. Lecithins are used in many food products, and they are also used in large quantities by the pharmaceutical industry.

Several commercial firms are working on the development of new uses for soybean oil and meal. In addition, the Northern Utilization Research and Development Division of USDA is exploring the soybean as a source of feed, food, and industrial products. One of its more promising discoveries is a way to make nylon 9 from soybean oil. Nylon 9 has many potential uses in the field of coatings and gears.

Soybeans on the Table

Consumers in the United States have little concern about the supply of protein. Meat and eggs, our primary sources of protein, are normally in plentiful supply. This is probably a major reason that the soybean has not figured more prominently as a human food in the United States.

In the Far East, however, where animal protein remains a luxury for the most part, soybeans have been a prominent part of the diet for centuries. The soy foods typical of that area include soy milk, soy sauce, sufu, miso, tofu, tempeh, kinako, natto, yuba, and others. Many of these products are the result of fermentation processes. Miso is allowed to ferment about nine months; tempeh ferments for only one day.

Whole soybeans are used as the starting point in making most of these products. Certain varieties of

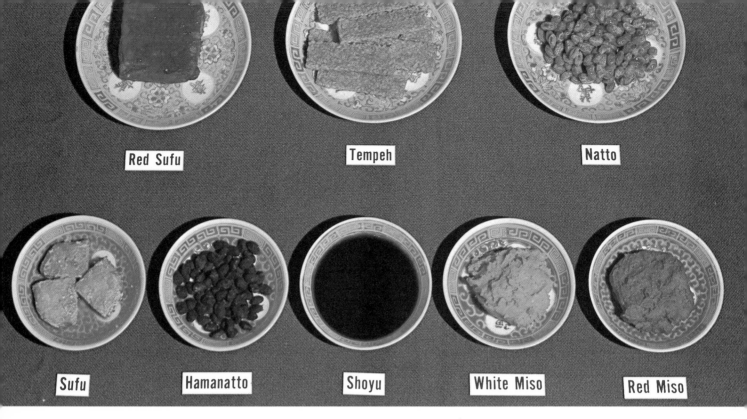

Red Sufu   Tempeh   Natto

Sufu   Hamanatto   Shoyu   White Miso   Red Miso

6. Numerous oriental dishes are prepared with soybeans. The special varieties for these uses are grown under contract in the United States.

soybeans are better suited than others because of factors such as flavor or yield of the final product. This is particularly true in the preparation of tofu and miso, popular foods in Japan.

During the last ten years several United States soybean exporters have specialized in supplying this market, which requires variety-identified soybeans of very good quality. Two varieties that have been in great demand for this market are Hawkeye and Kanrich. The latter is a large-seeded soybean developed originally for the domestic market for edible soybeans.

On-Farm Soybean Processing

The recent development of a relatively inexpensive soybean roaster or cooker for farm use has renewed the interest in feeding whole or ground soybeans on the farm. The raw soybean contains a trypsin inhibitor. Trypsin is an enzyme that is extremely important in the digestion of protein by animals. In nonruminant animals such as swine, the trypsin inhibitor interferes with normal protein digestion. If the inhibitor is killed by heat, as it is in the commercial preparation of soybean meal, nonruminants can utilize soybean protein as well as any other source. The inhibitor does not pose a problem to ruminants. Cattle can utilize the protein in noncooked soybeans equally as well as that in cooked soybeans.

With this knowledge, some midwestern dairymen have used uncooked soybeans for many years as a source of protein. This choice was not open to the swine farmer because of the presence of the trypsin inhibitor. The new on-farm processor and relatively small commercial processors give the swine farmer an opportunity to use his own soybeans as a source of protein.

There are other factors to be considered in feeding whole or ground soybeans. These include:

1. Feeding cooked soybeans to swine during the entire finishing period results in oily or soft fat, which is objectionable to the consumer. However, no such problem exists if the cooked soybeans are withdrawn from the ration and replaced by soybean meal when the hogs reach 150 to 160 pounds.
2. Soy oil may cause a laxative effect if the soybeans make up over 20 percent of a ration. This level of use, however, is abnormally high.
3. Soybean oil has a slight effect on milk fat, tending to make the butter softer, but this is not a problem at the consumer level.

A Look to Future Production

Plant physiologists and agronomists are beginning to unlock some of the basic secrets of soybean growth. As it is accumulated, this information will be used to develop higher yielding varieties and to improve the quality of the bean and the products made from it.

6 7

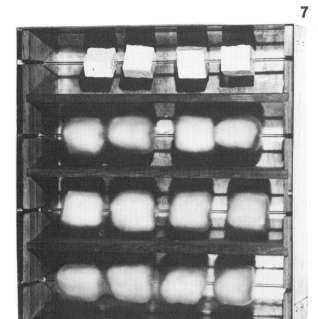

7. Tofu, a soybean curd, is inoculated with a fungus during the preparation of sufu. This dish has been a favorite among the Chinese for centuries. The top four cubes of tofu have not yet been inoculated.

8. The maintenance and expansion of export markets is vitally important to a healthy soybean industry in the United States. More than 40 percent of the country's soybean production goes into world trade.

8

9. Various studies of the process of photosynthesis are being conducted with soybeans. Better utilization of sunlight by the plant could be a key to increased yields.

Some of the important problems facing research workers are:

1. How to improve the photosynthetic efficiency of the soybean. The soybean converts only two to three percent of the light energy falling on an acre into yield.

2. How to reduce blossom drop. Under some conditions, yet to be accurately defined, soybean plants shed up to 75 percent of the blossoms they produce. It seems that yields could be increased if more flowers could be kept on the plant.

3. How to manipulate by genetic means the fatty acid content of the soybean. For instance, linolenic acid is the major precursor of off-flavors in soybean oil. Processors currently handle the problem. It would be more desirable for plant geneticists to breed out the inheritance of this feature.

4. How to change the oil and protein content of soybean varieties. Originally, a high oil content was important in establishing the value of soybeans. Now oils and fats are in surplus, so it would seem that high protein varieties would have a better place in the market.

5. How to reduce disease and insect losses. Geneticists constantly search for resistance to disease and insects, with the intent of developing resistant varieties.

6. How to improve the ecological balance of the soil. Some soil organisms, such as the nitrogen-fixing rhizobia, are beneficial; others, such as the fungus that causes brown stem rot, are harmful. Researchers are wondering if it is possible to provide a method of disease control in the soil, instead of in the plant.

7. How to improve the efficiency of nitrogen fixation. New, more efficient strains of rhizobia may be developed, as well as a method of inoculation that will insure nodulation by superior strains.

8. How to improve the soybean plant through biochemical and cytogenetic studies. Studies at the cellular level will yield information that may be the basis for developing new breeding techniques, such as commercial hybrid production. Or, they may result in information on disease resistance, insect resistance, and ways to increase photosynthetic activity.

9. How to improve the plant environment. More efficient fertilization is one such possibility.

There is seldom an immediate dividend from research. More often, several years elapse between the initiation of a research project and the application of the result on the farm. From 10 to 15 years are normally required in the development of a new variety.

10

10. Many unusual plants are found in the world collection of soybean varieties and strains. From this collection plant breeders get new genes for varietal improvement.

Appendix

Soybean acres harvested for beans (1,000)

	1960	1961	1962	1963	1964	1965	1966	1967	1968	1969
Alabama	133	146	149	156	161	228	280	484	557	641
Arkansas	2,409	2,554	2,682	2,923	2,981	3,550	3,728	3,989	3,989	4,228
Delaware	189	215	217	204	196	139	142	146	156	162
Florida	30	36	39	45	62	78	80	100	143	169
Georgia	75	80	80	91	120	209	301	542	542	472
Illinois	4,973	5,520	5,575	5,575	5,734	6,021	5,941	6,009	6,663	6,596
Indiana	2,415	2,681	2,708	2,735	2,817	2,871	2,814	2,898	3,246	3,278
Iowa	2,599	3,405	3,405	3,575	4,254	4,850	4,996	5,246	5,561	5,283
Kansas	586	703	914	832	691	873	917	825	957	852
Kentucky	199	201	219	234	260	295	310	388	466	485
Louisiana	216	197	219	296	423	622	871	1,306	1,436	1,608
Maryland	225	257	280	246	239	202	206	187	209	205
Michigan	221	285	351	330	343	440	480	509	463	514
Minnesota	2,090	2,341	2,201	2,377	2,852	3,166	3,356	3,591	3,232	3,167
Mississippi	916	1,044	1,107	1,317	1,291	1,461	1,797	2,120	2,120	2,290
Missouri	2,344	2,602	2,732	2,650	2,730	3,051	3,356	3,423	3,663	3,150
Nebraska	164	292	310	356	523	696	745	782	782	813
New Jersey	33	39	42	46	42	37	39	37	45	46
New York	3	4	4	4	4	3	3	4	6	5
North Carolina	545	568	558	608	681	776	923	1,117	972	933
North Dakota	176	185	67	151	192	211	236	290	215	185
Ohio	1,499	1,722	1,791	1,755	1,860	2,044	2,105	2,231	2,276	2,344
Oklahoma	124	157	171	150	136	152	143	164	184	204
Pennsylvania	7	9	9	6	8	16	18	22	22	25
South Carolina	499	604	710	710	746	806	879	1,046	931	959
South Dakota	100	125	123	149	252	333	346	370	300	258
Tennessee	394	463	553	528	586	732	871	1,115	1,193	1,193
Texas	75	86	66	72	63	82	123	258	312	262
Virginia	320	378	420	350	382	345	355	383	372	361
Wisconsin	96	109	107	109	125	160	185	185	161	174
Total (U.S.)	23,655	27,008	27,604	28,580	30,754	34,449	36,546	39,767	41,104	40,857

Soybean yield per acre (bushels)

	1960	1961	1962	1963	1964	1965	1966	1967	1968	1969
Alabama	24.0	24.0	20.5	21.0	23.0	22.0	24.5	27.0	22.0	23.0
Arkansas	21.0	19.0	21.5	17.5	20.5	21.5	22.5	23.0	22.0	20.5
Delaware	24.0	24.0	19.0	18.0	12.5	25.0	12.0	26.0	19.0	29.0
Florida	26.0	26.0	25.0	25.0	26.0	26.0	27.0	28.0	24.0	27.0
Georgia	17.0	17.0	16.0	16.5	20.0	20.5	23.0	24.0	15.0	24.0
Illinois	26.0	28.5	28.5	29.5	25.0	29.5	27.0	31.0	31.5	33.5
Indiana	27.0	28.0	28.0	27.5	23.5	28.0	26.0	24.5	32.0	32.0
Iowa	25.5	28.5	27.5	30.5	28.5	26.0	29.5	27.5	32.0	33.0
Kansas	21.5	21.5	17.5	14.5	17.5	21.0	22.5	22.5	25.0	23.0
Kentucky	22.0	25.0	24.0	24.5	22.5	24.0	25.0	28.0	26.5	28.0
Louisiana	24.0	24.0	22.0	22.0	19.0	21.5	25.0	23.0	27.0	19.0
Maryland	26.0	24.0	20.5	18.5	17.5	27.0	14.0	28.5	25.0	33.0
Michigan	20.0	26.0	22.5	21.0	22.0	22.0	22.5	20.0	26.0	23.0
Minnesota	19.5	23.0	19.5	24.5	20.0	18.5	24.0	19.5	22.0	24.0
Mississippi	22.0	22.5	19.5	19.0	19.0	22.5	23.5	23.5	27.0	22.0
Missouri	21.5	24.0	22.5	24.0	21.5	26.0	25.0	22.0	28.0	26.0
Nebraska	28.0	25.5	27.0	28.5	23.0	23.5	29.5	22.5	23.5	33.0
New Jersey	24.5	24.0	24.5	18.0	14.5	23.5	17.5	26.0	24.0	28.0
New York	17.0	21.0	18.0	16.0	17.0	15.0	20.0	23.0	22.0	21.0
North Carolina	22.5	23.0	24.0	23.5	24.0	25.0	25.0	24.5	17.5	26.0
North Dakota	13.0	18.0	13.5	19.0	14.5	19.0	22.5	13.0	15.5	16.5
Ohio	24.5	28.0	25.0	23.5	22.5	24.5	28.5	22.5	30.5	29.0
Oklahoma	20.0	19.5	16.5	13.0	15.0	16.5	20.0	22.0	21.0	17.0
Pennsylvania	23.0	23.0	21.0	19.0	18.5	24.0	19.0	27.0	24.0	30.0
South Carolina	19.5	20.5	19.0	17.0	23.0	21.0	22.0	22.5	12.5	22.5
South Dakota	17.0	18.0	20.5	24.0	16.0	17.0	20.0	16.5	17.5	24.5
Tennessee	22.5	22.0	22.5	21.0	23.0	23.5	24.5	25.0	21.0	24.0
Texas	27.0	26.0	28.0	31.0	28.0	26.0	27.0	26.0	27.0	29.0
Virginia	22.5	20.5	20.5	14.0	20.0	20.5	18.5	21.5	19.0	25.0
Wisconsin	16.0	18.5	18.0	17.5	15.5	19.0	20.0	18.0	22.0	19.0
Total (U.S.)	23.5	25.2	24.2	24.5	22.8	24.5	25.4	24.5	26.8	27.3

Source: USDA

Approximate pounds of selected plant nutrients in 12 leading crops

Crop and yield per acre	N	P₂O₅	P	K₂O	K	Ca	Mg	S	Cu	Mn	Zn
Soybeans											
grain 100 bu.	420	82	36	145	120	18	18	10	.10	.12	.10
stems, leaves, pods	140	27	12	97	80	—	—	—	—	—	—
Total	560	109	48	242	200	18	18	10	.10	.12	.10
Corn											
grain 150 bu.	135	53	23	40	33	2	8	10	.06	.09	.15
stover	100	37	16	145	121	26	20	14	.05	1.50	.30
Total	235	90	39	185	154	28	28	24	.11	1.59	.45
Cotton											
seed and lint 2,500 lbs.	70	33	15	25	20	3	7	3	.10	.20	.53
stalks, leaves, burs	52	15	6	52	44	42	12	—	—	—	—
Total	122	48	21	77	64	45	19	3	.10	.20	.53
Rice											
grain 130 bu.	76	18	8	18	15	5	9	4.8	.03	.18	.11
straw	34	14	6	103	86	13	7	—	—	2.24	—
Total	110	32	14	121	101	18	16	4.8	.03	2.42	.11
Wheat											
grain 40 bu.	50	25	11	15	12	1	6	3	.03	.09	.14
straw	20	5	1	35	29	6	3	5	.01	.16	.05
Total	70	30	12	50	41	7	9	8	.04	.25	.19
Rye											
grain 30 bu.	35	10	4	10	8	2	3	7	.02	.22	.03
straw	15	8	4	25	21	8	2	3	.01	.14	.07
Total	50	18	8	35	29	10	5	10	.03	.36	.10
Oats											
grain 80 bu.	50	20	9	15	12	2	3	5	.03	.12	.05
straw	25	15	7	80	66	8	8	9	.03	—	.29
Total	75	35	16	95	78	10	11	14	.06	.12	.34
Barley											
grain 40 bu.	35	15	7	10	8	1	2	3	.03	.03	.06
straw	15	5	2	30	25	8	2	4	.01	.32	.05
Total	50	20	9	40	33	9	4	7	.04	.35	.11
Sorghum											
grain 8,000 lbs.	120	60	26	31	26	2	10	11	.02	.08	.10
stover	135	28	12	153	128	27	14	18	.03	.15	.20
Total	255	88	38	184	154	29	24	29	.05	.23	.30
Alfalfa hay											
4 tons	180	40	18	180	150	112	21	19	.06	.44	.42
Coastal Bermudagrass hay											
8 tons	300	70	31	270	224	59	24	35	.21	—	—
Red clover hay											
2.5 tons	100	25	11	100	83	69	17	7	.04	.54	.36

Adapted from "Our Land and Its Care", National Plant Food Institute

Government reports concerning soybeans

Through the year the United States Department of Agriculture releases reports on soybean production, use, and holdings. The nature of these reports and their approximate release dates are as follows:

Title of report	Type of information	Approximate release date
Stocks of Grain	Stocks of soybeans in all positions as of January 1	January 24
Prospective Plantings	Planting intentions as of March 1	Mid-March
Stocks of Grain	Stocks of soybeans in all positions as of April 1	April 24
Field and Seed Crops, Production, Farm Use, Sales, Value	Soybeans produced, used on farms, sold, season average price and value of production	Early May
Crop Production	Preliminary planted soybean acreage as of July 1	July 10
Stocks of Grain	Stocks of soybeans in all positions as of July 1	July 24
Crop Production	Indicated yield per acre and indicated production of soybeans as of August 1	August 10
Crop Production	Indicated yield per acre and indicated production of soybeans as of September 1	September 10
Stocks of Soybeans	Soybean stocks report, listing soybeans in all positions as of September 1	September 24
Crop Production	Indicated yield per acre and total production as of October 1	October 10
Crop Production	Indicated yield per acre and total production as of November 1	November 10
Crop Production Annual Summary	Estimate of soybean acreage, yield per acre, and total production	December, third week
Crop Values	Crop values, including estimated seasonal average price per bushel and value of total production	Late December

In addition to the above, USDA publishes the Fats and Oils Situation, which incorporates a comprehensive view of the soybean situation, in January, April, July, October and November. Special statistical reports are issued, too, on an irregular basis.

All of these reports may be obtained without charge from Division of Information, Office of Management Services, U. S. Department of Agriculture, Washington, D. C. 20250.

Also available is the annual Agricultural Statistics, which reviews soybean production and use over a period of years. It is for sale at $2.75 by the Superintendent of Documents, U. S. Government Printing Office, Washington, D. C. 20402.

Grades and grade requirements for soybeans

Grade	Minimum test weight per bushel	Maximum limits of—					
		Moisture	Splits	Damaged kernels		Foreign material	Brown, black, and/or bicolored soybeans in yellow or green soybeans
				Total	Heat damaged		
	Pounds	*Percent*	*Percent*	*Percent*	*Percent*	*Percent*	*Percent*
1......................	56	13.0	10	2.0	0.2	1.0	1.0
2......................	54	14.0	20	3.0	0.5	2.0	2.0
3[1].....................	52	16.0	30	5.0	1.0	3.0	5.0
4[2].....................	49	18.0	40	8.0	3.0	5.0	10.0
Sample grade...........	Sample grade shall be soybeans which do not meet the requirements for any of the grades from No. 1 to No. 4, inclusive; or which are musty, sour, or heating; or which have any commercially objectionable foreign odor; or which contain stones; or which are otherwise of distinctly low quality.						

[1]Soybeans which are purple mottled or stained shall be graded not higher than No. 3.
[2]Soybeans which are materially weathered shall be graded not higher than No. 4.

USDA requires that the grade designation for soybeans include, in the following order, the number of the grade or the words "sample grade"; the name of the class; and the name of each applicable special grade.

The definition of numbered *grades* and *sample grade* are in the table.

There are five *classes* of soybeans: yellow, green, brown, black and mixed soybeans. The first four classes are described as soybeans which have seedcoats of their respective color (yellow and green are permitted for the yellow class) and which are of the same color in cross section and contain not more than 10 percent of soybeans of other classes. Mixed soybeans, the fifth class, are any soybeans which do not meet the preceeding requirements, including bicolored soybeans.

There are two *special grades* for soybeans. Garlickly soybeans contain five or more garlic bulblets per 1,000 grams. Weevily soybeans are those infested with live weevils or other live insects injurious to stored grain. The words "garlickly" or "weevily" are added to the grade designation of soybeans in cases where applicable.

Foreign material is defined as all matter, including soybeans and pieces of soybeans, which will pass readily through an 8/64 sieve (openings 0.125 inch in diameter) and all matter other than soybeans remaining on such sieve after sieving.

Adapted from the Official Grain Standards of the United States, Grain Division, Consumer and Marketing Service, U. S. Department of Agriculture, Federal Center Building, Hyattsville, Maryland 20782.

The soybean grower and the futures market

The futures market offers the soybean grower several financial opportunities. Before making any use of the market, however, a grower should be certain that he understands the nature and function of futures trading. It is a specialized field.

A soybean futures contract binds the seller to deliver a fixed amount of soybeans at a specified time. Similarly, it binds a buyer to accept delivery of the soybeans and pay the full contract price upon delivery. In practice, people who deal in futures generally do not intend to make or take delivery of soybeans. Both the buyer and seller can avoid making or taking delivery by executing an equal and opposite transaction in soybeans for the same futures month. This offsets the transaction and relieves the buyer and seller of all responsibilities under the contract. A soybean futures contract is for 5,000 bushels.

The speculative use of futures trading may appeal to the producer who has no storage and sells cash beans. He simply uses the money from the sale of his crop to buy soybean futures. If an anticipated increase in the futures price materializes, the grower makes money. If the futures price declines, he loses.

To understand and use the futures market as a more important part of the farm business, a grower must be familiar with the term *basis*. This denotes the difference between the Chicago futures price of soybeans and the local cash soybean price. It is caused by the costs of transportation, marketing, and storage. Basis is relatively predictable from year to year at a given location and date. It can be useful to a grower who wants to evaluate his prospects in futures trading.

For example, at harvest time a grower gets the futures quotation for July beans. He subtracts from this price the basis for his location in July, and compares that to the expected value of his cash soybeans in July. If the futures value appears to be greater than the expected cash value, the grower may want to enter into a futures transaction.

Using the Futures Market

Two important uses of soybean futures are fixing the price of a crop before planting and earning a return for storing soybeans. Both are forms of hedging.

In the first use, assume that it is early May and the grower, who has not yet planted his crop, expects to produce 10,000 bushels of soybeans. The January futures quotation is $2.60. Subtracting his basis, 20 cents, the grower arrives at a target price of $2.40. He is willing to accept this price for his beans, so he *sells* January futures for 10,000 bushels at $2.60. On November 15 he finishes harvesting and delivering his crop. The elevator pays him $2.25 per bushel. At the same time he *buys* January futures for $2.50 offsetting the contract he made in May. This means the grower has made a 10 cent per bushel profit on futures sold at $2.60 and bought at $2.50. The 10 cents is added to his price of $2.25 for cash soybeans, giving the equivalent of $2.35 a bushel.

A second good use of futures, the earning of a storage return, applies to a grower who stores his soybeans for marketing at some date after harvest. Soybean market history shows that cash prices often increase in the spring, but there is no guarantee of what level they will reach. Consequently, an element of risk is involved in storing soybeans. The risk can be minimized by advantageous use of the futures. The procedure is similar to that used before the soybeans are planted.

For example, assume that soybeans are placed in storage October 15, when the cash price is $2.07. July futures are quoted at $2.34, with a basis of 7 cents, leaving a target price of $2.27. On October 15 the grower *sells* July futures for $2.34. He stores his soybeans through the fall, winter, and following spring. On June 25 he sells his soybeans for $2.19 and *buys* July futures for $2.24. The futures, sold at $2.34 and bought for $2.24, earn the grower 10 cents a bushel. This, added to the cash price of $2.19, amounts to a gross of $2.29, or 22 cents a bushel over the October 15 cash price.

How the Broker Helps

A reputable, capable broker can explain additional uses to be made of the futures market. Brokers are licensed and government-supervised, but there are at least three points to be considered in selecting one. First, it may be advantageous to use one that is nearby, although brokers accept collect, long-distance calls without question. Second, some brokers do an excellent job of developing basis charts and spelling out hedging programs. Third, the individual broker should be selected on the basis of his understanding of what the farmer is attempting to do by dealing in futures.

Brokers' fees are no more than one-half cent a bushel, or $25 for a 5,000-bushel soybean contract. In addition, the farmer who deals in futures must pay a deposit of margin, normally 5 to 10 percent of the amount of the contract. Eventually, the margin deposit is refunded, plus or minus profit or loss on the transaction. If a grower sells a futures contract and the price increases, he may be called upon to put up additional margin. If he buys a contract and the price declines, he may be asked to put up additional margin deposit. A margin call, however, is not necessarily a reason for panic. For example, if a grower sells a contract and the price goes up, causing him to receive a margin call, he should remember that his cash soybeans in storage are increasing in value by a similar amount.

Planting capacity in acres per 10-hour day for various planters.

Planter	Speed and field efficiency											
	3 mph				4 mph				5 mph			
	50%	60%	70%	80%	50%	60%	70%	80%	50%	60%	70%	80%
	acres per 10 hours				acres per 10 hours				acres per 10 hours			
2-row 40 inches	12	15	17	19	16	19	23	26	20	24	28	32
4-row 20 inches	12	15	17	19	16	19	23	26	20	24	28	32
4-row 28 inches	17	20	24	27	23	27	32	36	28	34	40	45
4-row 30 inches	18	22	25	29	24	29	34	39	30	36	42	49
4-row 36 inches	22	26	31	35	29	35	41	47	36	44	51	58
4-row 38 inches	23	28	32	37	31	37	43	49	38	46	54	62
4-row 40 inches	24	29	34	39	32	39	45	52	40	48	57	65
8-row 20 inches	24	29	34	39	32	39	45	52	40	48	57	65
6-row 28 inches	25	31	36	41	34	41	48	54	42	51	59	68
6-row 30 inches	27	33	38	44	36	44	51	58	45	55	64	73
6-row 36 inches	32	39	46	52	43	52	61	70	54	66	77	88
8-row 28 inches	34	41	48	54	45	54	63	73	57	68	79	91
6-row 40 inches	36	44	51	58	48	58	68	78	61	73	85	97
8-row 30 inches	36	44	51	58	48	58	68	78	61	73	85	97
12-row 20 inches	36	44	51	58	48	58	68	78	61	73	85	97

Field efficiency indicates how much field time is spent planting. The greater the time spent in turning, filling seed hoppers, making minor adjustments and performing other jobs, the lower the field efficiency. Source: Purdue University

Plant population at row widths used for soybeans

Row width (inches)	Linear feet per acre	Plants per foot of row					
		12	9	8	6	4	3
7	74,674	896,088	672,066	597,392	448,044	298,696	224,022
10	52,272	627,264	470,448	418,176	313,632	209,088	156,816
14	37,337	448,044	336,033	298,696	224,022	149,348	112,011
20	26,136	313,632	235,224	209,088	156,816	104,544	78,408
21	24,891	298,692	224,019	199,128	149,346	99,564	74,673
24	21,780	261,360	196,020	174,240	130,680	87,120	65,340
28	18,669	224,028	168,021	149,352	112,014	74,676	56,007
30	17,424	209,088	156,816	139,392	104,544	69,696	52,272
36	14,520	174,240	130,680	116,160	87,120	58,080	43,560
40	13,068	156,816	117,612	104,544	78,408	52,272	39,204

Organizations pertaining to soybeans

American Soybean Association
P.O. Box 158
Hudson, IA 50643

National Soybean Processors Association
Suite 314
1225 Connecticut Avenue, N.W.
Washington, D. C. 20036

National Soybean Crop Improvement Council
211 South Race Street
Urbana, IL 61801

American Soybean Institute
P.O. Box 158
Hudson, IA 50643

American Soybean Association Research Foundation
P.O. Box 158
Hudson, IA 50643

Seventeen state soybean associations also
were in existence January 1, 1970.

Planting soybeans with a grain drill

Soybeans may be planted with a grain drill. The practice is particularly useful when planting in narrow rows. There are at least six arrangements for using a standard drill having 17 seed outlets 7 inches apart, and an overall width of 146 inches.

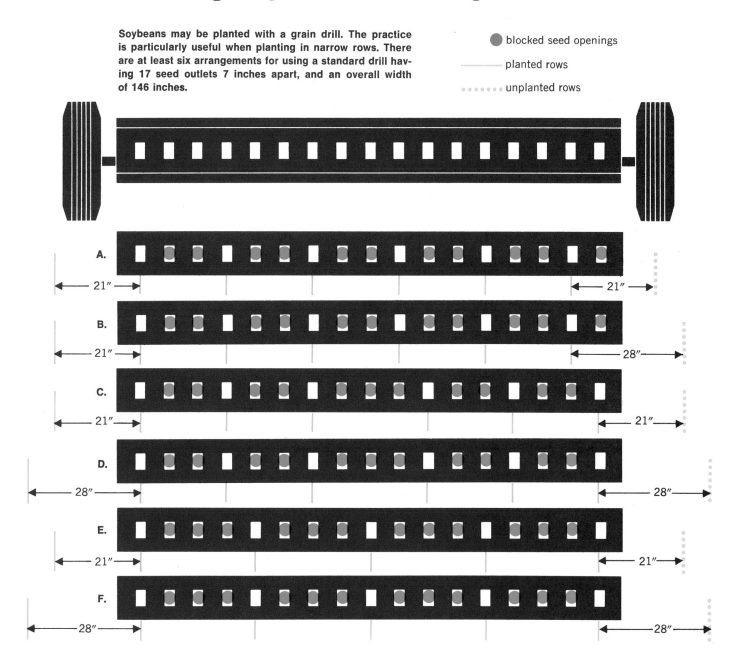

● blocked seed openings
—— planted rows
••••••• unplanted rows

Arrangement A. Six rows are planted on a 21-inch spacing. The drill is offset from the center of the tractor, so the row markers must be of different lengths. The last row planted on the right will be tracked by the transport tire on the return trip. Tractor wheel tread should be 84 inches.

Arrangement B. Same as A, but the tire tracking is eliminated. One 28-inch row is included.

Arrangement C. Six rows are planted with a majority of them on 21-inch spacing. The drill is centered behind the tractor and both markers are of equal lengths. Additional room is allowed for the front tires of a tricycle-type tractor, Tractor wheel tread should be 91 inches.

Arrangement D. Same as C, but the average row width is increased.

Arrangement E. Five rows are planted; some are 21 inches apart, some 28 inches. This layout is for a tractor with wide front end and special five-row cultivator. Rear tractor wheel tread should be 84 inches, front tread should be 63 inches.

Arrangement F. Same as E, but a consistent 28-inch row spacing is provided. Rear tractor wheel tread should be 84 inches, front tread should be 56 inches.

Adapted from *Narrow Row Equipment for Corn and Soybeans*, Cooperative Extension Service, Purdue University.

Useful information for calibrating sprayers

How to determine miles per hour

1. Stake off a distance of 88 feet (1/60 of a mile) in the field to be sprayed.
2. Select tractor gear and throttle setting to be used.
3. Using a stopwatch, clock the time required to drive 88 feet, from a running start.
4. Divide 60 by the time in seconds. The answer is miles per hour.

Converting broadcast rate to row basis

Unless specified otherwise, directions for the application of pre-emergence herbicides are given for broadcast coverage. If the herbicide is to be band-applied, the actual amount of solution to use per acre is calculated by the following formula:

$$\frac{\text{band width (inches)}}{\text{row spacing (inches)}} \quad X \quad \frac{\text{broadcast rate}}{\text{(gallons per acre)}}$$

Acres sprayed per tankful

Gallons per acre	Acres per tankful for various tank capacities, gallons									
	30	50	55	60	75	100	110	150	200	500
5	6.0	10	11	12	15	20	22	30	40	100
6	5.0	8.3	9.2	10	12.5	16.7	18.3	25	33.3	83.3
7	4.3	7.1	7.9	8.6	10.7	14.3	15.7	21.4	28.6	71.4
8	3.8	6.3	6.9	7.5	9.4	12.5	13.7	18.8	25.0	62.5
9	3.3	5.6	6.1	6.7	8.3	11.1	12.2	16.7	22.2	55.6
10	3.0	5.0	5.5	6.0	7.5	10.0	11.0	15.0	20.0	50.0
15	2.0	3.3	3.7	4.0	5.0	6.7	7.3	10.0	13.3	33.3
20	1.5	2.5	2.8	3.0	3.8	5.0	5.5	7.5	10.0	25.0

The acreage actually covered during band application of herbicide can be calculated by the following formula:

$$\frac{\text{acres per tankful X row width (inches)}}{\text{width of band (inches)}} = \frac{\text{crop acres}}{\text{band sprayed}}$$

Nozzle outputs (20-inch nozzle spacing*)

Output	Ground speed, miles per hour					
	3	4	5	6	7	8
5 gallons per acre						
Gallons per minute	.05	.067	.084	.101	.118	.135
Ounces per minute	6.4	8.6	10.8	12.9	15.1	17.2
6 gallons per acre						
Gallons per minute	.06	.081	.101	.121	.141	.162
Ounces per minute	7.8	10.3	12.9	15.5	18.1	20.6
7 gallons per acre						
Gallons per minute	.071	.094	.118	.141	.165	.189
Ounces per minute	9.0	12.1	15.1	18.1	21.1	24.2
8 gallons per acre						
Gallons per minute	.081	.108	.135	.162	.189	.216
Ounces per minute	10.3	13.8	17.2	20.7	24.1	27.6
9 gallons per acre						
Gallons per minute	.091	.121	.152	.182	.212	.242
Ounces per minute	11.6	15.5	19.4	23.3	27.1	31.0
10 gallons per acre						
Gallons per minute	.101	.135	.168	.202	.236	.269
Ounces per minute	12.9	17.2	21.5	25.9	30.1	34.4
15 gallons per acre						
Gallons per minute	.152	.202	.253	.303	.354	.404
Ounces per minute	19.4	25.9	32.3	38.8	45.2	51.8
20 gallons per acre						
Gallons per minute	.202	.269	.337	.404	.472	.538
Ounces per minute	25.9	34.5	43.1	51.8	60.2	69.0

*Data also applies if every other outlet is plugged and two nozzles are used per drop, as is often the case in post-emergence herbicide application.

The table may be used to:
1. Determine gallonage per acre at given ground speed and nozzle output.
2. Select proper ground speed when operating at a given nozzle pressure and output.
3. Select new nozzles when range of gallons per acre and ground speed is known.

Calibrating Granular Applicators

A useful method of calibrating granular applicators is to operate the equipment for a given distance while collecting the granules dispensed, then measure the volume of granules, and finally make adjustments to correct the application rate. For this technique a widemouthed bottle graduated in fluid ounces makes an excellent measuring container.

The operator should detach one delivery tube from the applicator spout and collect the granules that drop during 1,000 feet of travel. The granules can be collected in a paper bag attached to the hopper, or, in some cases, the jar may be attached directly to the hopper. After the granules are in the jar, it should be tapped gently to settle the material.

The desired amount of granules to be collected while traveling 1,000 feet is calculated by the following method: Multiply the width of the treated band (in inches) by the factor in the following table opposite the appropriate broadcast rate per acre.

Pounds per acre broadcast rate	Factor
10	.426
15	.639
20	.852
25	1.065
30	1.278
35	1.491
40	1.704
45	1.917
50	2.130

Example: To apply 25 pounds per acre in a 14-inch band, each spout should deliver 14.8 fluid ounces per 1,000 feet (14 x 1.065 = 14.8).

After this calculation has been made, the equipment can be adjusted to apply the proper rate.

Recommendations for granular herbicides and soil insecticides often are given only in terms of rate of active ingredient per acre. The adjoining table is useful in converting to pounds of product per acre.

If percent of active ingredients in granules is:	And recommended rate of active ingredients is: (pounds per acre)	Then apply this amount of granules (pounds per acre)
5	½	10
5	1	20
5	1½	30
5	2	40
5	3	60
5	4	80
10	½	5
10	1	10
10	1½	15
10	2	20
10	3	30
10	4	40
20	½	2½
20	1	5
20	1½	7½
20	2	10
20	3	15
20	4	20
25	½	2
25	1	4
25	1½	6
25	2	8
25	3	12
25	4	16

For example, if granules containing 20 percent active material are to be applied to supply one pound of active ingredient per acre, it is necessary to apply five pounds of granules.

Aircraft calibration

Acres covered per minute

Speed mph	Swath width in feet									
	30	35	40	45	50	75	100	200	300	500
75	4.5	5.2	6.0	6.7	7.5	11.2	15.0	30.0	45.0	75.0
80	4.8	5.6	6.4	7.2	8.0	12.0	16.0	32.0	48.0	80.0
85	5.1	5.9	6.8	7.6	8.5	12.7	17.0	34.0	51.0	85.0
90	5.4	6.3	7.2	8.1	9.0	13.5	18.0	36.0	54.0	90.0
95	5.7	6.6	7.6	8.5	9.5	14.2	19.0	38.0	57.0	95.0
100	6.0	7.0	8.0	9.0	10.0	15.0	20.0	40.0	60.0	100.0
110	6.6	7.7	8.8	9.9	11.0	16.5	22.0	44.0	66.0	110.0
120	7.2	8.4	9.6	10.8	12.0	18.0	24.0	48.0	72.0	120.0
130	7.8	9.1	10.4	11.7	13.0	19.5	26.0	52.0	78.0	130.0
140	8.4	9.8	11.2	12.6	14.0	21.0	28.0	56.0	84.0	140.0
150	9.0	10.5	12.0	13.5	15.0	22.5	30.0	60.0	90.0	150.0

The rate of application in gallons or pounds per minute is calculated by multiplying the acres per minute by the number of gallons or pounds per acre to be applied. Take for example a 100-mile-per-hour aircraft that has a 40-foot effective swath. The chart indicates that the plane has a coverage of 8.0 acres per minute. If spray is to be applied at a rate of 2 gallons per acre, the unit should be calibrated to dispense 16 gallons per minute (2 X 8 = 16). If 10 pounds of dry material is to be applied per acre, the unit should be calibrated to dispense 80 pounds per minute (10 X 8 = 80). The basic formula for calculating acres per minute is:

$$\frac{\text{swath width} \times 2 \times \text{miles per hour}}{1{,}000}$$

Conversion Tables

Converting research data to everyday terms

1 hectare = 2.5 acres
1 gram = 0.035 ounce
1 kilogram = 2.2 pounds
1 metric ton = 1,000 kilograms or 2,205 pounds
1 centimeter = 2.54 inches
1 meter = 39.4 inches
1 kilometer = 0.6 mile

Temperature conversions:

Centigrade = 5/9 (F — 32)
Fahrenheit = (C x 1.8) + 32

Common conversion factors

Multiply	By	To calculate
acres	43,560	square feet
cubic feet	1,728	cubic inches
cubic feet	7.48	gallons
cubic inches	16.39	cubic centimeters
cubic meters	1,057	quarts (liquid)
cubic yards	27	cubic feet
cubic yards	46,656	cubic inches
cubic yards	0.7646	cubic meters
feet	30.48	centimeters
feet	0.3048	meters
feet per minute	0.01667	feet per second
feet per minute	0.01136	miles per hour
gallons	3785	cubic centimeters
gallons	0.1337	cubic feet
gallons	231	cubic inches
gallons	128	ounces (liquid)
gallons	8	pints (liquid)
gallons	4	quarts (liquid)
gallons of water	8.3453	pounds of water
grains	0.0648	grams
grams	15.43	grains
grams	0.001	kilograms
grams	0.0353	ounces
grams per liter	1,000	parts per million
inches	2.54	centimeters
kilograms	2.205	pounds
kilometers	3,281	feet
kilometers	0.6214	miles
liters	61.02	cubic inches
liters	0.2642	gallons
liters	2.113	pints (liquid)
liters	1.057	quarts (liquid)
meters	3,281	feet
meters	39.37	inches
meters	1.094	yards
miles	5,280	feet
miles	320	rods
miles	1,760	yards
miles per hour	88	feet per minute
miles per hour	1.467	feet per second
miles per minute	88	feet per second
miles per minute	60	miles per hour
ounces (dry)	437.5	grains
ounces (dry)	28.3495	grams

Multiply	By	To calculate
ounces (dry)	0.0625	pounds
ounces (liquid)	1.805	cubic inches
ounces (liquid)	0.0078125	gallons
ounces (liquid)	29.573	cubic centimeters
ounces (liquid)	0.0625	pints (liquid)
ounces (liquid)	0.03125	quarts (liquid)
parts per million	0.0584	grains per U. S. gallon
parts per million	0.001	grams per liter
parts per million	8.345	pounds per million gallons
pecks	0.25	bushels
pecks	8	quarts (dry)
pints (liquid)	28.875	cubic inches
pints (liquid)	0.125	gallons
pints (liquid)	0.4732	liters
pints (liquid)	16	ounces (liquid)
pints (liquid)	0.5	quarts (liquid)
pounds	7,000	grains
pounds	453.5924	grams
pounds	16	ounces
pounds	0.0005	tons
pounds of water	0.01602	cubic feet
pounds of water	27.68	cubic inches
pounds of water	0.1198	gallons
quarts (liquid)	57.75	cubic inches
quarts (liquid)	0.25	gallons
quarts (liquid)	0.9463	liters
quarts (liquid)	32	ounces (liquid)
quarts (liquid)	2	pints (liquid)
rods	16.5	feet
square feet	144	square inches
square feet	0.11111	square yards
square inches	0.00694	square feet
square miles	640	acres
square miles	28,878,400	square feet
square miles	3,097,600	square yards
square yards	0.0002066	acres
square yards	9	square feet
square yards	1,296	square inches
ton	907.1849	kilograms
ton	32,000	ounces
ton	2,000	pounds
yards	3	feet
yards	36	inches
yards	0.9144	meters
yards	0.000568	miles

Index

188

189

Credits

Editor, Bill Barksdale

Layout and design, Barron Krody

Special drawings, Ikki Matsumoto

Cover photograph, Bill Barksdale
Frontispiece, Bill Barksdale

1

Facing page, Billie Seamans
1. Ikki Matsumoto
2. Seed Technology Lab, Mississippi State University
3. W. O. Scott
4. Billie Seamans
5. S. R. Aldrich
6-8. W. O. Scott
9, 10. Alan Linn
11, 12. W. O. Scott
14, 17. W. O. Scott
18. Ikki Matsumoto
19. W. O. Scott

2

Facing page, Harris Barnes
1. Ikki Matsumoto
2. S. R. Aldrich
3-8. W. O. Scott
11, 12. W. O. Scott
13. Bill Barksdale
14. W. O. Scott
15. Ikki Matsumoto
16, 17. University of Illinois

3

Facing page, Bill Barksdale
1. Billie Seamans
2. Ikki Matsumoto
3. Barron Krody
4. White Farm Equipment Co.
5. Charles Bailey
6. Billie Seamans
7. H. L. Musen
8. Deere and Co.
9. Bill Barksdale
10. Brillion Iron Works, Inc.
11. University of Illinois
12. Side-Winder
13. Bill Barksdale
14. J. I. Case Co.
15. Bill Barksdale
16. Iowa State University
17. Robert D. Walker
18. W. O. Scott
19. Barron Krody

21. W. O. Scott
22. Barron Krody
23, 24. Ikki Matsumoto
25. W. O. Scott
27. W. O. Scott
28. Harris Barnes
29. Nitragin Co., Inc.
30. W. O. Scott
31. Ikki Matsumoto

4

Facing page, American Cyanamid
2. Barron Krody
3. University of Illinois
4-6. Barron Krody
7. Tennessee Valley Authority
8. Barron Krody
9. Ikki Matsumoto
11. Barron Krody
12. Ikki Matsumoto
13, 14. Barron Krody
15. S. R. Aldrich
16. American Cyanamid
17. S. R. Aldrich
18, 19. Barron Krody
21. S. R. Aldrich
22. Billie Seamans
23. S. R. Aldrich
24, 27. Barron Krody
28. Bill Barksdale
30. W. O. Scott

5

Facing page, Bud Fichte
1. Ikki Matsumoto
3. Bill Barksdale
4. A. L. Lang
5. J. B. Fehrenbacher
6. J. W. Pendleton
7. David Young
8, 9. Harris Barnes
10-12. Ikki Matsumoto
13. S. R. Aldrich

6

Facing page, Billie Seamans
1, 2. W. O. Scott
3. Ikki Matsumoto
4. W. O. Scott
5. Ikki Matsumoto

6. Billie Seamans
7. Harris Barnes
8. W. O. Scott
9. Harris Barnes
10. University of Illinois
11. Billie Seamans
12. Amchem Products, Inc.
13. Harris Barnes
14. W. O. Scott
15. Harris Barnes
16. Delta Branch Experiment Station
17. Harris Barnes
18. Billie Seamans
19. Harris Barnes
20. Bill Barksdale
21. W. O. Scott
22. Bill Barksdale
23. E. L. Knake
24. Bill Barksdale

7

Facing page, Harris Barnes
Page 126. Ikki Matsumoto
1. Iowa State University — USDA
2. University of Illinois
3, 4. Bill Barksdale
5, 6. F. A. Laviolette
7. W. O. Scott
8. F. A. Laviolette
9. W. O. Scott
10. University of Illinois
11-15. W. O. Scott
16. Bill Barksdale
17. H. B. Petty
18. Bill Barksdale
19-30. H. B. Petty
31. David Young
32-34. H. B. Petty
35. C. A. Thomas
36. H. B. Petty
37. David Young
38. USDA Oilseeds Insect Lab
39, 40. H. B. Petty
41-43. S. R. Aldrich
44. C. D. Foy and Agronomy Journal
45. S. R. Aldrich
46. Noble Usherwood
47. S. R. Aldrich
48. E. L. Knake
49-51. W. O. Scott
52. University of Illinois
53. W. O. Scott

8

Facing page, Harris Barnes
1. Bill Barksdale
2. Tom Huheey
3. Bill Barksdale
5. W. O. Scott
6, 7. Tom Huheey
8, 9. W. O. Scott
10. Tom Huheey
11. Barron Krody
13, 14. Malcolm Emmons
15. Harris Barnes
16. Barron Krody
18. Bill Barksdale
19. Tom Huheey
20. Ikki Matsumoto
21. Barron Krody
23. Ikki Matsumoto

9

Facing page, Vince Hill Studio/ Central Soya
1. U.S. Northern Regional Research Laboratory
2. Worthington Foods
3. Barron Krody
4. Alan Linn
5. Bill Barksdale
6, 7. U.S. Northern Regional Research Laboratory
8. Bud Fichte
9. J. W. Pendleton
10. S. R. Aldrich